Bob Ogley, Mark Davison and Ian Cu

The NORFOLK
and SUFFOLK
Weather Book

On 9th August, 1843, East Anglia endured a tempest of great fury and intensity. It was followed by a fusillade of hailstones which "caused such a fearful scene of elementary strife and such heaviness to many a heart" that something had to be done to alleviate the distress, particularly in Norwich. The city fathers had a brilliant idea. They created an "insurance company". It was called the General Hailstorm Insurance Society, later to merge with other companies under the umbrella of the Norwich Union. Those who joined would no longer have to bear the cost of the damage brought about by the "frequent wicked acts of nature". In the years to follow there were more tempests, and tornadoes, more hailstones, and heatwaves, there were floods and freezes, deluges and dust-devils — weather that has wreaked havoc right across the beleaguered counties of Norfolk and Suffolk. In this unique pictorial record of those dramatic events, we have the evidence.

Supported by

**NORWICH
UNION**

Froglets Publications
and Frosted Earth

Froglets Publications Ltd, Brasted Chart,
Westerham, Kent TN16 1LY.
Tel: 0959 562972   Fax 0959 565365

© 1993

Bob Ogley, Ian Currie and Mark Davison

ISBN 1 872337 99 6 (paperback)
ISBN 1 872337 98 8 (hardback)

Cover illustrations

Front cover: A motor car partly submerged at Martham, Norfolk in the great floods of 1938.

Back cover: Rushmere Church, Suffolk on 14th January, 1987 by courtesy of East Anglian Daily Times.

This book was originated by Froglets Publications of Brasted Chart and Printed and bound by Staples of Rochester Ltd. Hardback edition bound by Green Street Bindery.

Jacket design by Alison Stammers

Additional research, editing and design by Fern Flynn

Acknowledgements

FOUR radio stations in East Anglia — BBC Norfolk, BBC Suffolk, SGR FM and Radio Broadlands — allowed us to appeal over the air for reminiscences about dramatic meteorological events. The response was fantastic. From all corners of the two counties came anecdotes, old photographs and newspaper cuttings about the famous and lesser known blizzards, floods, tornadoes and heatwaves. Local newspapers also published our appeal for help and those who replied confirmed to us that East Anglia is well renowned for the great variety in its weather.

Many other people gave us advice and practical help and special thanks go to Norfolk meteorologist, Norman Brooks of Old Costessey, local historian Gordon Anckorn of Dersingham, Robin Sharp of the Royal National Lifeboat Institute and the East Anglian Division of the National Rivers Authority.

We are particularly indebted to David Kindred, Ken Blowers, Sharon Boswell and Robert Diamond of the East Anglian Daily Times, Alan Atherton and Derek James of the Eastern Daily Press, Alistair Murphy of Cromer Museum, the staff of the Norfolk Museum Service, Cathy Beck of Illustrated London News, Rosemary Rogers, Kerry Meal and the staff of the Suffolk Record Office in Ipswich, Bury and Lowestoft, David Williams and Theo Cutting of the Bury Free Press, Ford Jenkins of Lowestoft, the staff of the Museum of Country Life at Stowmarket, Aldeburgh Museum, Dunwich Museum, Dick and Penny Shannon, Norfolk and Suffolk Fire Services, Anglian Water, English Heritage, Norfolk and Suffolk County Councils, British Rainfall, Climatological Observers Link, Royal Meteorological Society, Meteorological Office, Mrs Cynthia Gibling, Mr J.H. Willis, Mr Dereck Edwards, Dr Charles Briscoe, Mrs Margaret Buttle of The Bull, Yaxley and the Library staff throughout the two counties.

We referred to many books, in particular — The Floods of 1812, The Journal of Meteorology, Weather in Britain by Robin Stirling, Pickwick Papers by Charles Dickens, Poppyland, Tall stories of Lowesoft by Jack Rose, Suffolk Scene by Julian Tennyson, The photographs of Violet Farley, Shell Guides to Norfolk and Suffolk, North Sea Surge by Michael Pollard, Great Tide by Hilda Grieve, Weather Patterns in East Anglia.

Photograph credits

East Anglian Daily Times
62,63,91,99,118,119,142(top),143,145,155(bottom),162.
Gordon Anckorn 68,109(bottom),138(top). **K.P.Boulton, Boulton-Hawker Films** 69. **Jean Overson** 70(right). **Marlene Mills** 73(top). **Vernon Place** 136,137,139.
Eastern Counties Newspapers 75,76,79,80/81,82, 84,86(bottom),87,88,90,92,93,95,96,100,107, 112,113,115,116,123,126,127,131,132,133,134,137&138(bottom), 141,142(bottom),144,153,154,155,157,158,159(bottom),160,162(bottom)163,164.
Topham Picture Library
73,83,85,86(top),89,94,101,104,110(bottom),111.
Norfolk Chronicle 103. **K.Gunn-Ray** 108. **Nigel Bloxham** 128, 129. **Lynn News** 130. **H.J.Mothersole** 147. **Holly Pelling** 148. **Roy Buttle** 149. **Duncan Morris** 150. **Cynthia Gibling** 151 **Cambridge Evening News** 161.
Suffolk Record Office 7,10,12,13,19,22,23,25,26,27,29,30(top),32,33,35,36 (top),40,47,51,55 (top),64 (top),66,70,97. **D. Kindred** 8,64 (bottom),102,125. **Cromer Museum** 9,15. **RNLI** 16. **British Post Office** 14. **Illustrated London News.** 20 **National Railway Museum** 42 (top). **Ford Jenkins** 24 30,34,39 .**Seckford Collection** 24 (bottom),28. **Brian Girling** 37. **Norwich Library** 42 (bottom),43 (bottom),45(top),46 (top). **Bury Free Press** 53,55 (bottom),110,159. **J.Claydon** 54. **E.E.Swain** 109. **Viola Farley** 56

THE WEATHER IN EAST ANGLIA

Not always wild and wicked...

ON 31st January, 1953, a storm surge driven by north westerly winds of hideous ferocity crashed against the east coast sea defences which were progressively overwhelmed as the surge travelled south. For the people of Norfolk and Suffolk it was the worst weather disaster in their history. Thousands remember the misery and the horror of 1953 when the winds roared, the sea heaved and smashed to pieces thousands of tons of stone and concrete, drowning more than 100 people as they desperately tried to clamber, or swim, to safety

The consequences of the disaster to farmers, industrialists, coastal traders, those who had seaside homes and those responsible for the east coast defences, were far reaching. But was it an isolated event of a magnitude never previously experienced and therefore unlikely to be repeated?

In this book we describe how the east coast of England has always been a battleground in the unceasing conflict between the land and the sea. Tidal disasters have occurred frequently throughout history. The total number of lives lost have been very great — not only on the coast but along the tidal creeks, estuaries and rivers where flood waters probe deep, attacking towns and villages on flank and rear.

It is not surprising that, to the people of East Anglia, the weather is a perpetual topic of conversation. That interest is not only confined to floods and tidal surges. The people of North Norfolk have seen a whole range of extreme conditions for the marshy lands, warm and benign in summer, are notorious for heavy snow in late winter and sometimes, early spring. The great blizzard of 1881 produced snow so deep that cars and trains were buried and many people perished. In more recent times, who can forget the remarkable snowfalls of 1963 and 1987 ?

Norwich has experienced almost every weather variation possible — thunderstorms, hailstorms, whirlwinds, tornadoes and great floods, like that of 1912, when 7.5 inches of rain fell in 48 hours and blizzards, so furious that the city has been paralysed. On the Broads, holidaymakers have cruised, basked in the sunshine and enjoyed the gentle breezes in summer but have been completely oblivious of the winter floods which have turned rivers and dykes into vast areas of watery wastes. In 1938, in the biggest coastal breach for 50 years, more than 15 square miles of land was inundated and the village of Horsey was evacuated.

In Suffolk there have been such phenomena as whirlwinds, dust devils, ice storms and even earthquakes. South east Suffolk felt the shock waves from the 'quake that hit Colchester in 1884. The county has taken the full impact of the furious winds and blizzards such as the memorable winter of 1947 when snow, sub zero temperatures and overcast skies gave two months of gloom and hardship to the people of Suffolk. When the great snows thawed there were floods that brought tragedy to Fenland.

Ipswich has been flooded often. In the days of great deluges — and there have been many — the Gipping and the Orwell have burst their banks and flooded homes, causing heartbreak and chaos. The worst of all was, perhaps, the "tropical monsoon" of January 1939 when 78,000 acres of land received as much as 429 million gallons of water. It depends on the age of the reader but what was more disastrous than that brought about by the torrential rainfall of September 1968 ? Certainly the people of Sudbury, Haverhill and Bury will never forget their "storm of the century".

At the other extreme are the long, hot summers when temperatures soared into the nineties, a thousand fires developed, rivers and reservoirs ran dry, garden hoses were banned and the East Anglian coast from King's Lynn to Felixstowe was invaded by hordes of holiday makers. The years shout out to be remembered. 1947, 1959, 1976, 1989 and 1990.

Then there was the drought when the perils of too much swirling waters were exchanged for the menace of subsidence as clay soils dried out right across East Anglia. Cracked rivers beds, dried up reservoirs, stringent water restrictions and vanishing wildlife supported the theory of global warming in the most prolonged drought, and one of the major meteorological events, of the century.

The Norfolk and Suffolk Weather Book is the fifth in our County Series. Like its predecessors it could not have been compiled and published without the co-operation of the general public, who responded to our appeal for reminiscences, anecdotes and photographs. From all over the two counties came proof of the great variety of weather for which East Anglia is renowned.

We would like to thank the staff of libraries and museums. local history enthusiasts, meteorological experts and editors and photographers of newspapers throughout the region.

Particularly, we are indebted to the Eastern Daily Press in Norwich, the East Anglian Daily Times in Ipswich, the Bury Free Press and the Suffolk and Norfolk Record Offices whose staff allowed us access to their archives and provided many of the illustrations that illuminate the text.

CONTENTS

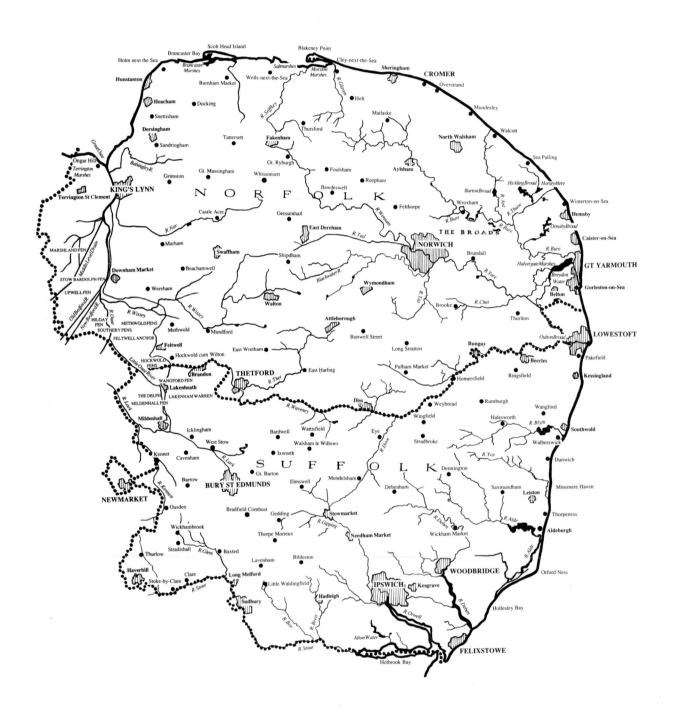

CHAPTER ONE: 1200 — 1799

Early battles with the waves

1236: A great tide pounded at the east coast, accompanied by a storm of unabated fury. The chronicler, Holinshed, wrote: "It washed up the ocean in such tremendous waves that the banks gave way and the whole country lay completely exposed to its awful fury". Shipping was damaged, trees uprooted, entire flocks of sheep and herds of cattle were drowned, houses destroyed and beaches swept away. The toll of human life was appalling. According to Holinshed "in one village there were buried one hundred corpses in one day".

1287: More than 100 people were drowned at Hickling in Norfolk when the sea surged into the village in the the middle of the night. Men, women and infants were drowned or suffocated in their beds and "many, when surrounded by the waters, sought a place of refuge by mounting into trees, but benumbed by the cold they were overtaken by the water and fell into it and were drowned".

1362: A violent "hurricane" blew down the upper part of Norwich Cathedral steeple and caused considerable injury to members of the choir. Bishop Percy gave £400 out of his own purse for reparation.

1613: "A dreadful inundation of the sea on 13th November", laments the historian Dugdale. Norfolk marshland sustained appalling damage. At Terrington the collapse of the sea banks was total and the town suffered enormous losses. Dugdale records that "a bridge was shattered, over 2,000 head of livestock drowned, 480 acres of land sown with corn were swamped and 13 houses ruined". During the same storm the three mile-long bank at Walpole was breached in 20 places. The total losses suffered by Norfolk Marshland exceeded £37,000.

1619: An appeal was made to the country on behalf of the Southwold fishermen, whose harbour had suffered "through the violence of the water."

1668: Santon Downham was overwhelmed by a sand storm which covered more than 1,000 acres, the whole area "having the appearance of a beaten sea coast without the least vegetation".

1713: From Norwich Cathedral Records of 15th February : "The high wind blew down the north-west pinnacle of the tower which in its fate made a great breach in the roof of the north aisle.

1739: A "long hard winter" in which the coast from Essex to Newcastle was "strowed" with wrecks through damage caused by wind and ice. A contemporary writer said: "In that terrible winter there were scenes of greater damage than has ever been known in the memory of man."

1762: More than 300 houses and eight parish churches were inundated during the "great Norwich flood" which rose 12 feet perpendicular in 24 hours. It was 15 inches higher than a similar flood in 1619 but lower by 13 inches than in 1613.

1770: A great storm occurred early in the morning of 18th December and at daybreak 18 ships were seen on a sandbank off Lowestoft, "half of which number went to pieces before 9 o'clock". It is estimated that 200 sailors were drowned.

1786: A white Christmas. On Boxing Day, Parson Woodforde of Norwich wrote in his diary: "Very sharp frost last night and this morning. It froze the water in my basin that I wash in quite over, in half an hour after it had been brought upstairs."

1798: Another white Christmas. Turkeys, in abundance, sold at 7d per lb in Norwich market. Parson Woodforde wrote: "We have not had so severe weather for years. I can scarce live in it. No beds warmed either. Frost in the parsonage. Milk and cream icy. Meat like blocks of wood."

Storm claimed the lives of 8,000 people

THE storm which struck England on 26th November, 1703 and wrought havoc from Cornwall to Kent has often been described as "the worst hurricane ever known." The writer Daniel Defoe captured the full horror in a documentary account in which he described how carriages were blown into fields, boats were lifted out of rivers onto dry ground, warships were destroyed and more than 8,000 people killed. The tempest was considered to be a token of Divine displeasure. By the time it had reached East Anglia it had blown out a great deal of its fury but King's Lynn lost seven ships and 20 men perished. Damage sustained to buildings in the town was considered to be at least £1,000. It also tore the roof from Ely Cathedral but Bristol suffered worse than any other city "because of the overflowing of the tide".

Seas roar and the towns topple

A THOUSAND years ago, in the days of Edward the Confessor, a great gale crashed against the already-crumbling shores of East Anglia and caused devastation and heartbreak. The coastal people of Suffolk and Norfolk, driven from their homes, watched in dismay as their towns and villages were torn into ugly, shapeless lumps of brick and stone and then devoured by the gluttonous waves. When the tide calmed and the flood waters receded, men strained their brawny shoulders to the breach. They fought, they worked, they attempted to rebuild their homes, but great waves, driven by another North Sea storm, returned to crash and snarl against the shore. Those hardy men abandoned their task and retreated; the cruel and impassive enemy had won again.

The story of Dunwich, Eccles and Shipden (as told on pages 8 and 9) is synonymous with the story of East Anglia. For 30 years, perhaps, the North Sea will hold back and the fear of a great storm surge will die away until a complacent generation has forgotten it altogether. Suddenly, the wind and the seas will roar in unison and a gale will rise to hell-born force. The bulwarks will collapse, the cliffs will crumble and a torrential flood will rush in across the marshes. Nature has altered the east coast — there is no limit to the damage she can do.

The story of east Norfolk is an unhappy one. Between Cromer and Happisburgh the coast is wasting rapidly. Since the Norman Conquest the original villages of Keswick, Clare and Wimpwell have disappeared. Overstrand and Sidestrand suffered disastrously in the Middle Ages and are still suffering. Cromer was once an inland town, while Shipden, on the seaward side of Cromer has gone.

The long serrated ridge of sandhills between Horsey and Palling has been repeatedly pushed back. At times Horsey Mere and Martham Broad have become part of the sea. The villages of Walcott, Palling, Eccles and Waxham have all suffered from erosion. The original site of Eccles, like that of Shipden, is under the sea. It was obliterated years ago and the church tower long stood as a solitary memorial of the vanished village. That was blown down in 1895. A few miles farther north the waves roll over the old village of Happisburgh, which stood north eastwards of its modern successor.

In November, 1800 the Kings Arms Inn on Sheringham cliff "fell a prey to the waves" and in November, 1810, more land was lost. "A tremendous gale of wind and high tide", wrote the *Norfolk Remembrancer*, "the breach from Yarmouth to Wells covered with dead bodies washed ashore."

Along the Suffolk coast, from Lowestoft to Felixstowe, there is not one town or village which has not suffered seriously from the inroads made upon it by the sea. The harbours at Easton and Minsmere have been lost forever while those at Orford and Bawdsey have silted up and disappeared, bringing fisheries and shipping to a dismal end. Towns toppled long ago to premature destruction. Pakefield, Covehithe and Easton Bavents hardly exist at all. Julian Tennyson, writing about Suffolk in 1936 said of Covehithe: "All that you will find today are a few cottages on top of the cliff and, besides them, the ruins of a tremendous church. It is an amazing skeleton this, and almost perfect; a huge tower, the walls of the aisles with their tall. elegant windows and in the crumbling wall of the chancel one of the largest windows I have ever seen in a parish church."

At every town or village it is the same tragic story. Blythburgh and Walberswick were once places of prosperity and influence but today Walberswick is a small village with a few attractive old houses clustered round the quay and at Blythburgh there is nothing save a few houses, a hotel and the finest church in east Suffolk.

The sea has gnawed the heart out of Orford, Bawdsey and Aldeburgh. At Aldeburgh there were three streets running parallel with the beach but one has been destroyed with the exception of the ancient Moot Hall. The adjoining hamlet of Slaughden has suffered and so, too, has Orford. This was a place of great importance, a fine fishery and a port that sent many strong ships to the help of the English fleet. Gradually the harbour was blocked up and destroyed altogether. Tennyson wrote: "What torture it must have been to the men of Orford to watch in impotent despair while their prosperity decayed before their very eyes, and to pass their lives in wondering whether their sons or their grandsons would be the first to feel the pangs of ruin. About all that is left in Orford now is an oyster bed."

Felixstowe has offered little resistance to the wind and the waves. The greater part of the parish called Walton has been washed away since the time of the Romans. A small harbour called Wadgate is recorded to have existed in the reign of Edward III, but of this, too, there is now no trace.

"Oh, so slowly does the sea beleaguer us", wrote Tennyson. "Could you see it in summer, drawling up the beach, brushing the shingle with coquettish lips, so gentle, so harmless, so indolent, you would scoff at the idea of evil lurking in that serene and imperturbable bosom. But come to it in the winter, when the same innocent sluggard is cold and grey, when the fishermen stand helpless on the beach beside their little boats and the wildfowl chatter uneasily in the safety of the rivers and the marshes — come back then and see how dreadful is the change from meekness to ferocity".

A child sits in the middle of St Magarch Road, Dunwich on a summer's day in 1865. In the background is the church. Road and church were to become victims of the waves.

Coldest day "in the memory of man"

16th January, 1740

FOR sheer length and ferocity the winter of 1739-40 ranks as the most severe since 1700. At the end of December, according to contemporary reports "there blew a gale straight from the heart of Russia and the temperature fell to the coldest day in the memory of man". The bitter east wind caused ice to form three inches thick in just 24 hours. Across eastern England the gale was accompanied by temperatures estimated to be below 15F (-9C). In Holland a reading of 0F (-18C) was recorded.

Large trees were split apart by frost on 16th January as the skies cleared and the wind dropped. Ice formed on the Thames in London and the gale drove it up the river so hard that it formed into a vast pile of blocks and remained frozen for seven weeks. At sea, some sailors lost their fingers due to frostbite and ships were covered in ice with their ropes encased in frozen spray as thick as the mast.

There was terrible devastation along the east coast, particularly at Dunwich where a vast amount of the cliffs was washed away along with the last remains of the St Nicholas churchyard and the road leading into town from the quay. For mile upon mile, sand and shingle distributed by the sea took the place of pastures and arable land. The Cock and Hen Hills, some 40 feet high the previous summer, were levelled to the ground.

The grim winter of 1740 continued into March and the spring was frosty. Poorer folk in East Anglia suffered from diseases such as scurvy, owing to destruction of vegetable crops. At Marsham, in Norfolk a phenological diary recorded an extremely late date for the arrival of hawthorn blossom — 8th June.

The city beneath the waves

TODAY Dunwich is a small village which nestles behind a sandy cliff. Tracks of Roman roads lead to it across the heaths. There is a sandy beach where holidaymakers bathe and laze and watch the foam-topped waves roll and slide. In the summer the sea is innocent and subdued but in the winter, the great white waves crash and snarl against the shore. Fishermen watch from the beach for they know that these same storm-driven waves have taken all that Dunwich ever had. The finest city in East Anglia is "somewhere out there under the sea".

Coastal erosion has been going on for hundreds of years along the east coast. Thanks to courage and enterprise, Southwold has been saved but nowhere is the destruction so complete as it is at Dunwich — - and it was going on long before the violent storm and bitter winter of 1739-40.

The city beneath the sea was once a place of magnificence and wealth, East Anglia's first capital 1,300 years ago. This gated, ramparted town which, in King John's day, was only slightly smaller than Ipswich "had 52 churches, chapels, religious houses and hospitals, a King's Palace, a Bishop's seat, a Mayor's mansion and a mint; as many topships as churches and no fewer windmills".

All lie wave-battered and tide-mauled, mere lumps of masonry on the sea bed. There is nothing left but legend, speculation and a handful of relics. The houses which line the village can be counted in a few seconds. There is a post office, a hotel, a fish and chip shop, tea rooms. Nothing more. That is Dunwich today.

Historians record that the battle with the wind and the sea started "at an exceedingly early period" when the church of St Felix and a cell of monks were lost. A storm and a rough sea caused further devastation in 1282. The church of St Martin and St Nicholas went in the fourteenth century along with 400 houses. In 1535 the sea "eat away the shore near to Blackfriars". In 1540 the church of St John the Baptist had to be moved and before that century ended "not one quarter of the town was left standing". By 1677, the sea had made its way to the market place. The town hall fell in 1680, the Church of St Peter in 1702, the gaol in 1715. There was a forest called Eastwood which went the same way.

In 1740 came the biggest storm of all. It exposed the foundations of St Francis' Chapel and the secret repositories of the dead were strewn about as the sea 'surged and boiled'.

By the beginning of the 20th century only the ruins of All Saints Church with the ivy-clad fragments of a Franciscan friary was left of a town which from 1296 to 1832 returned two members of Parliament. Today, those ruins have gone.

There would always have been time for the bells and other valuables to be removed but the more romantic maintain they can hear the muffled sound of ringing bells — from deep on the ocean bed.

The last church in Dunwich to be claimed by the sea was All Saints which, at the beginning of the twentieth century, stood on the side of the cliff. The ruins have now gone the same way as all the other churches and houses in the once-fine town — down the gullet of that vicious sea.

Fashionable Cromer as it looked at the turn of the century. The Great Eastern Railway had reached the town and the area, known as "Poppyland", attracted thousands of visitors each summer who were able to see how North Norfolk was rapidly being engulfed by the sea.

Those in peril by the sea

IN Norfolk, too, there are church ruins deep down on the sea bed. On the north coast, the site of the parish church of Shipden now lies about half a mile out to sea. The ruins of Eccles church disappeared after a storm in January 1895 and only its foundations can, on occasions, be seen. A similiar fate has overtaken Palling. There was a village near Eccles called Markesthorpe which has disappeared completely.

Shipden, first mentioned in the Domesday Book and a companion town to Cromer, is probably the most famous for its fate. At one time it was a bustling port with a fleet of trading ships swinging at their moorings. In the 15th century its mariners were still plying a brisk trade with Iceland and Norway, but the sea was always threatening and navigation became so dangerous and difficult that a pier was built. To pay for it the King granted the men of Shipden the right to levy duties on all merchandise entering the port.

Then came the bad times. Each year the storms grew fiercer and fiercer, or so it seemed. By 1551 so much " had the rages and surges of the sea swallowed up the town" that a petition for aid was addressed to the Privy Council. Help came but to little avail. The howling wind and huge tides were still thundering against the church and erosion became so serious that a jetty had to be built for the defence of the local fishing boats.

A century and a half later the sea was still at grips with the community they knew as Cromer "alias Shipden". The erosion could not be stopped. The jetty disappeared and a futile attempt was made to build a new one. A third attempt, also fruitless, was made in 1731. Eventually the old town disappeared, unable to compete with the frenzy of the tide and the winds.

The effects of incursion by sand are most spectacular in Eccles. There the dunes have passed completely over the church. Captain King wrote in his diary on 27th December, 1862: "To the north of the church considerable remains of cottages are laid out: the very roads and ditches are visible....The old tower now stands clear of the sandhill in which it was embedded." On 1st May 1869 he wrote: "I made a careful study of the church. At that time the foundations were perfect."

On the night of 19th October, 1869 there was a north-easterly gale and high tide. The foundation of the church was undermined and turned over on its side. Attempts to preserve it proved fruitless.

The battle continues today. In 1993, The Anglian Region of the National Rivers Authority, responsible for coastal protection, said they intend to invest £340m in new defences. These will have to be capable of withstanding, not only the potentially severe surge tides, but also the rise in sea level and the increase in storms which scientists predict will result from global warming.

No mercy for the mariner

FOR more than 500 years the east coast winter gales have taken a fearful toll of Britain's shipping. Wreck charts show that the East Anglian coast has sent more ships and more luckless mariners to their graves than all the concealed rocks and jutting headlands of Cornwall and Wales. A galaxy of craft has been strewn around the coastline from the Wash to Felixstowe — oar-assisted galleasses, trim-looking frigates and sloops, gainly brigantines, swift sailing schooners, ponderous collier brigs, barques, smacks, high powered yachts and mighty full-rigged ships. The majority have been victims of the weather.

From this disastrous panorama of shipwrecks we have chosen a selection of those who have suffered from nature's violence. Why did these brave mariners so frequently risk their lives? Perhaps they had little choice. When out on the deep they either had to trim the sails and face the storm or turn and run for the nearest shelter in port or headland.

On one terrible night in 1692 no less than 200 ships and more than 1,000 men went down in The Wash and along the North Norfolk coast. On Christmas Eve 1739, 16 ships were driven ashore between Lowestoft and Yarmouth. In 1770, again in December, 18 vessels were blown out of the safe channels and on to the treacherous sandbanks where they were broken up by towering waves. On this occasion the wind had suddenly changed from south-west to north-west and blew so strongly against the Suffolk coast that no anchor or cable was strong enough to hold a ship against it.

In such storms, boats in the open sea were overwhelmed. In 1739 at least 130 fishing smacks and coasters were sunk or wrecked between Cromer and Southwold. In his book *East Anglia Shipwrecks,* Stan Jarvis writes: "Would-be rescuers were totally frustrated as they looked across the raging seas to shout words of encouragement to seamen who had taken to the rigging of a doomed vessel. Another great wave would come pounding in and when they looked again the rigging was empty."

In the eighteenth century, the volume of traffic passing through the German channel was vast. Coal from Newcastle to London was the most important coastal trade and by its very geographical position the East Anglian seaboard saw a greater passage of ships than any other part of the English coast. If the wind and sea caused most disasters then a contributory factor was the deplorable condition of many ships. So long as a vessel would float the owners kept her trading with precious little thought for the lives or safety of her crew.

The *Nautical Magazine* of December 1867 says: "Something ought to be done with the wretched, rotten colliers that crawl along this coast at the instance of mercenary men who care more for money than human life".

These harsh words were well justified. During the previous year, 1866, there were gales in January, February, March, October, November and December and the number of disasters occurring round all the coasts of Britain numbered 2,289. Of this appalling total 953 happened on the east coast — an average of nearly 20 wrecks a week.

Altogether nearly 1,000 lives were lost and lifeboatmen were continuously being called upon. No wonder there was such a demand for more stations to be placed all round the East Anglian coast.

So the long list of casualties at sea, and the adherent heartbreak on land, continued to mount — through the nineteenth century and into the twentieth. Gradually the age of "floating coffins" passed because ships were now built of steel and self propelled and seamen refused to sail in those that were likely to break up in the face of those bitter tundra winds that came driving in from the north. That did not stop the oil tanker *Olcades* from being brought ashore at Walcott, or the collision in foul weather between two super tankers, the *Roseline* and *Eleni V* in which escaping oil covered six square miles and fouled the beaches all the way from Yarmouth to Aldeburgh.

Such accidents today are the exception rather than the normal way of things so when a ship does have the misfortune to collide, or come aground or suffer in a storm, she at once becomes front page news, but, so long as there are vicious winter winds and treacherous waves there will always be shipwrecks off the coast of Norfolk and Suffolk.

These nine sailors were lucky. They were rescued by the Southwold Lifeboat from The Idun after a harrowing ordeal in rough seas on 17th January, 1912.

CHAPTER TWO: 1800 — 1899

Century of storm and tragedy

1805: A whirlwind produced mayhem at Rockland St Mary. A rowing boat lying on a bank of the Broad was lifted into the air and propelled a distance of 70 yards. A young man suffered similar treatment.

1807: A heavy fall of snow rendered the roads impassable on 11th February and the mail from Newmarket was unable to get through. The guard of the mail rode across country with the mail bags and, from Bury, took a poste chaise to Norwich. He arrived at 4 pm the following day. In August a storm at Norwich produced such a cloudburst that "the roaring of the waters falling from the roof to the lower leads of the Cathedral was so tremendous as to drown the noise of the thunder that accompanied it".

1809: A rapid thaw on 28th January led to an inundation of parts of Norwich. Boats were needed in the street at St Martin-at-Oak where the water was six feet deep. A violent gale the next day blew down a chimney and killed the occupants of a house in Cokey Lane. A large tree, planted on 30th January 1649 — the day that King Charles I was beheaded — blew down.

1810: The beaches were strewn with wrecks and the bodies of "unfortunates" from Wells to Yarmouth after a great gale on 2nd November. During another gale on the 10th, Captain Manby's life-saving apparatus saved 18 seamen.

1818: A south-easterly gale blew out a window at the church of Pulham St Mary on 4th March. December was remarkably mild and, it was reported, the cuckoo was heard.

1827: A heavy snowfall on 15th January led to the demise of hundreds of rabbits in the Thetford and Brandon district through being out in search of food and unable to find their burrows again.

1830: A great frost commenced on Christmas Eve and was so severe that, in just 48 hours, mill streams and rivers became frozen solid and navigation between Norwich and Yarmouth was obstructed by ice.

1833: An assembly place for astronomical observations was struck by lightning during a severe thunderstorm at Butters Hill, Norwich. The Black Tower was, according to an eye witness, set alight by a fireball the size of a man's head. It consumed the thatched roof and destroyed valuable apparatus.

1836: A great Christmas blizzard.

1838: A tempest struck the great oak at Necton and felled two branches, the size of ordinary trees. At Carbrooke, a windmill was wrecked and a man killed. On 11th October, a severe gale saw 2,000 ships seeking refuge in the Yarmouth Roads and so much food was needed for the sustenance of the sailors that butchers were obliged to kill every bullock and sheep that they could find.

1840: During an unusual winter storm on 21st January a woman was struck by lightning at Carlton Road, near Attleborough and her clothes set on fire.

1841: The thermometer in January fell to zero degrees on the old scale at Norwich and fowls, under cover, were frozen to death. The month ended remarkably warm and brilliant but the cold came back with a vengeance and by 3rd February, navigation was stopped by ice at King's Lynn.

1843: On 16th June "the sun was surrounded by a bright and beautiful halo with several others appearing in the vicinity". A whirlwind occurred at Blakeney on 8th July.

1846: A hot summer. On 4th July the heat was so great that ironwork on the Swing Bridge at Trowse expanded, preventing it opening for river traffic.

1861: Severe weather with 12 inches of snow on 6th January. The mayor of Norwich inaugurated a fund to relieve the distress of the poor. At Breydon a large

---

A furious squall on 24th February, 1837 drove the *Raby Castle*, bound from London to Stockton, onto the beach at Salthouse, near Sheringham and she became a total wreck. She had a rich cargo; spirits, wine, oranges, nuts, hampers and toys bestrewed the beach.

There was wholesome plunder with one group pouring spirits over each other in drunken revelry. Even coast guards, assigned to guard the wreck, became intoxicated and many were conveyed from the beach dead drunk. Of the £5,000 worth of cargo only £800 was recovered.

The village school at Capel St Mary, south of Ipswich was struck by lightning during a storm in 1854 and totally destroyed. It was rebuilt.

Snow in May, 1871

(1800 - 1899 cont)

party assembled on the ice and "skated" quadrilles.

1863: A gale of unusual violence on 2nd December left hardly a house in Norwich undamaged. Off the coast 142 men and boys were drowned.

1865: A slight earthquake was felt from Scratby to Lowestoft.

1866: A new gasholder of 100,000 feet capacity and surrounded by massive iron columns was blown over at Yarmouth during a gale. The year ended with a heavy snowstorm and many roads in East Anglia were impassable.

1870: Another cold Christmas. After a mild spell, the temperature plunged to 5F (—15C) on Christmas night. There was a fall of deep snow.

1871: A storm of great violence on 10th February led to the loss of many vessels and left no clue as to their names or ports to which they belonged. The storm petrel was seen. Snow fell on 17th May.

1875: Owing to a wet November and a heavy fall of snow in early December which then melted, the Waveney Valley at Geldeston was deeply flooded. The lock-keeper had only a few square yards of dry land. On this he killed more than 100 rats and a great number of moles.

1877: A severe gale at sea on 30th January with many fishing boats lost. 112 seamen perished.

1878: A disastrous flood occurred in Norwich on 15th November from the combined effect of rapidly melting snow, heavy rain, gales and high tides. Hundreds of the city's inhabitants were forced to flee in boats and several lives were lost.

1879: A fearful storm on 2nd August destroyed Wells Church when it was struck by lightning. This was one of the coldest years of the 19th century.

1881: The year of the great blizzard which began on 18th January with winds "assuming the strength of a hurricane". Road and rail communications came to a halt with 10 foot drifts. There was loss of life.

There was a devastating gale across Norfolk on 28th May, 1860. Twenty vessels belonging to Yarmouth and Lowestoft were lost and 200 men and boys drowned, leaving 240 women and children in destitution. On land some 1,500 trees were levelled at Blickling and the windows of Cromer Church blown in. Christmas 1860 was one of the coldest on record. The mercury fell at Costessey to 39 degrees fahrenheit below that at which water freezes.

Sunshine weather for a Queen

Queen Victoria celebrated her Diamond Jubilee in brilliant sunshine on 22nd June, 1897. Enthusiastic crowds gathered in every town and village in East Anglia to join in the festivities, including Southwold which is pictured here. In Norwich 9,000 children assembled in the market place and sang. Costume cricket matches were played on many local grounds and hot air balloons made frequent ascents. Newspapers reported the event in great detail. "For 60 years Queen Victoria has provided the stability which others countries can only dream about, and during her reign the empire has expanded to become the largest and richest the world has ever seen."

1884: Great heat was experienced on 11th August — reaching 95F (35C) at Norwich.

1886: Considerable damage was caused to telephone wires in Norfolk by a heavy fall of snow on 28th December. "The whole system came to grief", it was reported, "through the wires breaking and the derricks giving way.

1888: An extraordinary year with snow in July and a mild spell in early December. A correspondent wrote to *The Times*: "I am still supplied with green peas grown in my garden at Brundall, the roses are in flower, the fields abound in primroses and wild flowers". The cuckoo was said to have been heard at North Elmham and strawberries were gathered at Swainsthorpe on Christmas morning.

1890: An intensely cold spell began in late November and continued throughout December. Skating became general. From 25th to 28th November, 16 inches of snow fell at Ipswich.

1891: On 1st January the frost broke after 21 consecutive days, but began again the following night. Gradually, milder weather returned and on 24th January the river steamer Alpha was able to cut her way through the ice on the Yare and open up the river traffic between Norwich and Yarmouth which had been suspended for five weeks. On 10th January an "ice carnival" took place on Diss Mere and spectators numbered 5,000. At Whitsun there was a memorable snowstorm but on 13th May the mercury had been as high as 73F (23C). Four days later it had plunged to 37F (3C).

1892: On 21st October, Norfolk experienced a heavy fall of snow.

1894: A year of three severe gales. A snow-laden storm from the north-east during early January caused great hindrance to traffic and many casualties were reported on the coast. A few days later, on the 12th, a storm blew from the south-west and there were widespread casualties, particularly among the Yarmouth fishing fleet. In December, gales from the 21st to the 29th led to enormous tides. At Mundesley it was the largest ever known.

1895: A severe cold spell in February, freezing the River Deben. There was much skating.

White Christmas at Dingley Dell

THE two Christmas blizzards of 1830 and 1836 were immortalised by Charles Dickens (born 1812) as the "Dingley Dell snowstorm" in Pickwick Papers. A graphic, if quaint, description of the latter classic white Christmas is contained in an old weather book, written by the late Orlando Whistlecraft of Thwaite, near Eye in Suffolk.

"On the 25th December, 1836, at night, a violent hurricane from the north-east, with the greatest fall of snow ever known over all England. The roads were completely blocked up to the depth of from four to nine feet here, and in some places from 20 to 50 feet!

"The stop to all business was distressing, all the mails delayed for a week and no passage could be found from one place to another till the labourers were everywhere employed to excavate a cut through.

"A great and general visitation of sickness prevailed after the great thaw (which commenced on the 6th January following), and business was nearly as much stopped by it as by the snow before. The medical men termed it "the influenza" being an epidemic catching from the air more than from each other, and this continued from about the 5th January, 1837 to the end of the month with a great number of deaths."

It was during the 1836 snowstorm that an avalanche occurred at Lewes in Sussex — the only one ever recorded in the history of lowland England. Snow, which had piled up on top of the South Downs suddenly swept down and buried a number of cottages below. Fifteen people were trapped under many tons of snow and eight lost their lives.

Storm that brought the curtains down

9th August, 1843

SUCH was the fierceness of the great thunderstorm which broke out over the city of Norwich on 9th August, 1843 that the performance at the Theatre Royal was stopped, cellars and basements blocked with ice and hail, thousands of glass houses shattered, crops destroyed and gardens cut to pieces. According to the *Norwich Chronicle* "very old men have never before witnessed so fearful a scene of elementary strife, carrying desolation to many a dwelling and heaviness to many a heart."

The tempest burst over Norwich at 7.30 and "thunder and lightning commingled with rain and hail to a degree that produced sensations of awe and fear in the boldest spectator". On this violent evening the rain fell in torrents and morsels of ice covered the ground to a depth of four to five inches. "It fell in such profusion", said the *Chronicle* "that nothing could be seen through the falling mass.

"In the Red Lion district, the Coach and Horses suffered, for the torrent rushed into the ground floor and loosened a sort of quicksand beneath the cellars and the beer barrels sank into an abyss. At the Bell Hotel on Orford Hill, a hundred squares of glass were smashed whilst a poor woman was literally carried off her feet by the torrent down the hill. The grocery stores in the Old Haymarket were inundated and, during the night, four cartloads of ice were taken out of the shop and cellars."

"At the Theatre Royal the performance was stopped by the fierceness of the storm; for the thunder and

THE NORWICH Mail *in a Thunder Storm* 1827

This stamp, issued in 1984 to commemorate the bicentenary of the mail service shows the Norwich Mail in a thunderstorm, similar to that of 1843.

lightning were not of the stage variety on this occasion. With frightened actresses and alarm among the audience, the curtain was dropped until the violence of the tempest abated. Lakenham factory suffered from a hail fusillade and no less than 700 panes of glass were shattered. The Market Place was like a huge lake and the water rose a foot in five minutes in the Bishop Bridge locality."

All round the county there was a disastrous catalogue of crops spoiled, mills damaged, trees uprooted and widespread floods. The tale of havoc showed that in some places the hailstones were as large as pigeons' eggs.

Norwich Union — story of a hailstorm

THE great hailstorm of August, 1843 proved a disaster for Norfolk. Farm buildings were ruined, glasshouses shattered and thousands of acres of crops destroyed.

For the beleaguered farmers, there was no compensation and, so serious was the situation, the city fathers got together, assessed the degree of damage, introduced a voluntary county rate for the sufferers and recommended the formation of an insurance company.

In the first prospectus the company was designated as the Norwich Hail, but the scope of the enterprise speedily took wider lines and the title General Hail was adopted. It officially came into being in November, 1843, with an authorised capital of £200,000 in 8,000 shares of £25. The head office was in Bethel Street, Norwich.

The company quickly went from strength to strength absorbing, before the end of the nineteenth century, other hailstone insurance societies. In 1898, General Hail was amalgamated with the Norwich and London Accident Association and, in 1908, with Norwich Union Fire, which had been established in 1797. These companies were eventually incorporated under the umbrella of the Norwich Union.

From that fusillade of hail 150 years ago was born a company that was to become the third largest insurance group in the UK and among the top ten in Europe. By 1993 it had funds under management of £27 billion and was one of the top five institutional investors in Great Britain.

Ten engines forced a passage through the snow

A snowstorm on 4th January, 1854, which was accompanied by a severe gale from the east north-east, provided flakes so huge and so dense that navigation on land and sea was well nigh impossible and huge drifts built up, particularly in the Fens where inhabitants were reported to be in "a most distressed condition".

For the railway companies the situation was so grim that one train needed eight engines in order to force a passage through the snow. Even so it came to a standstill after half a mile. The Norwich mailtrain was more successful, thanks to the efforts of 260 men and the use of ten engines.

At sea the severe gale led to great loss of life with 50 vessels driven ashore. One of them was the *Abraham* which foundered a short distance from Gorleston Pier. There was no lifeboat and no means to effect a rescue so the unfortunate crew clung to the rigging for three hours before finally succumbing to the waves. In London, masses of ice impeded navigation on the Thames and at Greenwich, the mercury fell as low as 13F (-10C).

Driven by storm-force winds, this collier, The Hero, crashed into the old jetty at Cromer in December 1897. The jetty was eventually sold as scrap and the new pier built in 1901.

The Rescuer collides with a shipping lugger and turns turtle. Twenty six men died in this tragedy on 2nd December, 1867

Disaster strikes twice for Yarmouth

THROUGH the centuries, the storm-battered coast of East Anglia has been a graveyard for many fine ships. Countless men and women have lost their lives — victims of fire, war, bad luck, bad judgement and, on most occasions, the weather. Thousands more would have died if it were not for the gallant deeds of the Norfolk and Suffolk lifeboatmen who have provided some of the most heroic and spectacular rescues on record — and, on occasions, themselves become victims of the gales.

In January 1866 and again in December 1867, tragedy befell the Yarmouth and Gorleston Lifeboat Station twice leaving a community in a state of deep shock. This is what the *Norfolk Chronicle* said shortly after the second incident.

"Yarmouth Bar has again been the scene of a catastrophe, exceeding in the intensity of its horrors and destruction of human life even that which occurred nearly two years ago, which it resembled in some of its circumstances, the chief actor, if such a term can be applied to an inanimate object, and the scene of the occurence in each case being the same.

"On that occasion (13th January) the lifeboat, bearing what must now be deemed the inappropriate name of *The Rescuer* whilst racing out of the harbour with a rival boat in pursuit of salvage struck on the Bar and capsized, 13 of the crew perishing in sight of their comrades who were powerless to help them.

"On Tuesday (2nd December), she was returning into harbour having nobly performed her duty and bearing, it was thought into safety, the crew of a shipwrecked vessel, when just as the haven was nearly reached, by some mischance, which the contradictory evidence at the inquest fails to make clear, she came into collision with a shipping lugger entering the harbour from a contrary direction, and capsized.

"Six of the crew who manned her shared with the captain, mate and 18 of the crew of the *George Kendal*, the watery grave from which it was believed a moment before, they had saved them. Five of the men were married and 13 children are fatherless orphans for whose future support an appeal will be made. We feel confident it will elicit as noble a response as that which attended the application on behalf of the sufferers by the disaster of January 1866."

On these two occasions, the sea claimed 39 lives.

Norwich folk told 'your city cannot flood'

NOVEMBER 1878 was wet, very wet. From the 1st to the 16th "twas mist and rain and storm and mist" throughout Norfolk. Rain gauges in many places measured six inches for that period and rivers became swollen. The people of Norwich watched the water level rising but they were not unduly concerned. Hadn't they been told that improved engineering and drainage had freed the city from such a disaster as a flood?

By 16th November immense volumes were pouring into the River Yare and overflowing into the lower Wensum Valley. The upper Wensum, swollen by the down-coming waters from mid-Norfolk, spread rapidly beyond the marshes on to the Heigham Causeway.

As Saturday evening closed on Norwich, those in the danger zone had only enough time to escape to their upper rooms as water cascaded along numerous streets towards Dereham Road. A young man named George Churchill lost his life as the water rose. William Buck, a tailor, tried to wade up the road but was washed away and drowned.

A contemporary account of the flood said: "Strange to say, the calamity which had befallen the city was hardly known outside those streets that were actually inundated. People going to church on the Sunday morning were amazed to find sheets of water in the streets and to behold carts and boats bringing people from their waterlogged homes. Many a deed of heroism was performed that Sunday by worthy citizens, who often plunged fearlessly into the water to help women and children into the boats."

Orchard Street (top) and Napier Street in the great floods of 1878

Trains lost in a great blizzard

18th January, 1881

A snowstorm of extraordinary violence swept Norfolk and Suffolk in January, 1881. The whole of East Anglia, with other large parts of England, was buried under enormous drifts which, in places, were 20 feet deep. Lives were lost, trains buried and hundreds of villages cut off for up to a week after the blinding storm deposited undreamed of quantities of snow.

The month became bitterly cold after the first week and many parts of the country had a few inches of snow on the ground by the second week. By mid-morning on Tuesday 18th January, savage easterly winds were whipping across the Fens and within hours the East Coast stood in the path of a remarkable Arctic-like storm "the likes of which had not been known by anyone alive at the time".

The gale, from the Continent, was relentless. It blew in billions of tiny grains of snow — not flakes — but minute particles like sand which were remorselessly blasted against homes, shops and farms. They penetrated the tiniest crevices and cracks and formed snowdrifts inside houses and workplaces. Railway cuttings were completely filled and the snow heaped up to such an extent that sometimes only the funnels of buried trains could be seen. Across England it was estimated that 100 people perished.

The *Bury Free Press* commented that a Scotsman living in Suffolk could not recall anything like it back home. By the evening, the winds were so high and the blizzard so intense that pedestrians "could only get along by doggedly holding down their heads and taking the chance of running against somebody or something. To see the way was impossible".

Chimneys crashed down in Bury during the day but in the evening the damage became far more extensive. The roaring winds blasted the snow off fields and into country lanes, blocking them in minutes. Soil was also lifted off the Fens and driven onto roads. Two newspaper reporters set off from Bury in a fly in an attempt to get to Ixworth for a meeting but they were forced to abandon their trip at Banton Road "the driver being unable to see his horse or the road or anything else through the driving snow". On turning round he was confronted by another fly driver on the wrong side of the road who "knew not where he was or where he should have been".

A train, due to arrive at Bury St Edmunds at 7.14 that night, eventually pulled in at 2 am but this was a remarkable achievement. Many trains were stuck fast and the driver of an omnibus had to ask a gang of labourers to dig him out of drifts at Alpheton. Tragedy beset the town of Yarmouth, yet again, when the crew of the lifeboat *Abraham Thomas* perished at sea while attempting a rescue. They had fearlessly launched into the heavy seas to try to save the crew of the *Guiding Star*, which had gone aground. While endeavouring to haul the vessel back to the beach the lifeboat suddenly capsized and spectators on the shore were horrified to hear the cries of men as they struggled in the water. "Although a stone's throw from safety six of the poor fellows were drowned, including the mate of the *Guiding Star*, leaving 21 children with only mothers to bring them up."

Another vessel at Yarmouth also went ashore on the beach. The *Edith Marian* loaded with coal was abandoned by some of the crew who plunged into the water and were hauled out of the breakers by spectators. Five were saved and five feared drowned. At Gorleston, thousands of people lined the shore to watch the unsuccessful attempts of the lifeboat crew to rescue seven— including a woman — from the *Battle of Corunna*. "With aching hearts they had to leave the dreadful scene. As the chill afternoon light faded, all efforts had to be abandoned and the hands on this coal vessel died in a frozen state."

In fearful conditions, the Harwich Lifeboat crew set out to give assistance to a barque in distress. The foaming seas upturned the lifeboat and the crew spent a considerable time in the icy waters. One member was swept more than two miles away and died from exposure. The others were saved.

There was much damage to property in Ipswich. A chimney crashed through a building in Balcon Street. A porter in Tavern Street was lifted by the wind off his feet. The hands of the Town Hall clock were blown away and sheets of lead from houses on the Norwich Road were "twisted like paper".

At Lowestoft, fires were started in the Post Office after debris crashed down the chimney. There was extensive damage to buildings. At Kessingland Beach, an Austrian barque set sail into the teeth of the gale. All hands but one perished within 15 minutes.

At Southwold, it was reported that the force of the wind was unprecedented. "The ocean was white with foam as far as the eye could see." Spectators gathered to watch another stricken vessel, the *Martinus Marie* from South Shields. With its sails torn to shreds, "it was heartrending to see the poor fellows, eleven in number, lashed to the rigging,

(continued)

The blizzard of 1881 provided some of the worst weather conditions of the nineteenth century.
The photograph shows children and a horse carting water from a pond at Culpho Hall,
Playford in Suffolk, probably in a later severe winter.

utterly helpless and out of reach of aid. The rocket apparatus was brought into operation, line after line being projected from the mortar and, as a last resort, the lifeboat was launched, but before she could reach the scene, the surf had carried away the mizenmast with seven men lashed to it and the vessel split up like matchwood." Three of the men were washed up alive; two were carried to the Lord Nelson Inn and one to the villas on the cliff. The rest perished.

In Norwich, trains and mailcarts were many hours late. The morning train to Cromer was blocked by a drift between Worstead and North Walsham — a picture repeated all over the county. In places passengers were led to safety from the immobilised trains but often the snow was far too deep. A grand skating match at Wroxham Broad had to be cancelled and, in parts of Cromer, snow was seven feet deep.

At Corton, between Lowestoft and Great Yarmouth, a schooner, *Eliza Jane*, carrying 100 tons of potatoes to London parted from her anchors. The man in the rigging was so frozen it is believed he lost his grip and was washed away. Another man was so benumbed with cold, he was unable to raise the alarm and was washed overboard. In less than an hour of the SOS, the vessel broke up into numerous pieces.

Many homes lost their roofs in Aldeburgh and crewmen were plucked from the sea, or from their doomed crafts. Sixteen men were rescued from a Russian ship but two died. At Felixstowe, a vessel foundered without warning and disappeared.

There was much grief in Boxford, near Hadleigh where the Tower Windmill was smashed to pieces. Throughout East Anglia, market squares were piled high with snow dug from shopfronts and soup kitchens were set up to help the poor and starving.

The severe spell of weather gripped the two counties until 27th January when less cold conditions brought relief from what was, arguably, the greatest blizzard of the entire nineteenth century.

This sketch, drawn during the gale at Lowestoft on 28th October, 1882, was reproduced in the Illustrated London News of 11th November.

The tragedy of 'Black Saturday'

28th October, 1882

THE great storm which roared across the North Sea on a furious October day in 1882 made such a lasting impact that, years later, old seafarers "trembled with emotion" when they recounted the dramas and disasters of the day they called Black Saturday.

The fury of the storm littered the East Anglian coastline with wreckage. Many fine men and countless ships were lost. It was a day on which landsmen could witness at close quarters something of the havoc caused at sea. It was certainly a day to be remembered.

The morning of 28th October was hideous. Torrential rain was lashed along by a strong north-easterly and there were ominous white crests on the waves which crashed over the sandbanks and hit the cliffs like a battering ram. Vessels in the North Sea quickly shortened sail and made for the shelter of Yarmouth Roads — but as the gale increased in strength, ship after ship began to be driven before the howling wind.

Anxious spectators, aware of the direction and force of the storm, gathered at vantage points along the coast and watched the ships, as they were driven towards treacherous sandbanks with their anchors dragging. At Lowestoft harbour an estimated 3,000 people watched the disaster unfold before their eyes.

Brigs, schooners, steamers, ketches and fishing boats crashed into each other or were driven aground in a chapter of disasters that lasted all day. Some sailors took to their small boats and managed to reach safety. Some swam to the pier while others were rescued by coastguards who successfully fired rocket lines to the sinking ships.

There were, however, many casualties which increased in number as the gale raged on. The ship *Warrior Queen* from Newcastle went down with all hands and the brigatine *Sovereign* lost seven crew, victims of the infamous Newcome Sands. The steamer *Secret* suffered the same fate and three members of the brig *Isis* were swept away. A fishing boat *Zenith* disappeared without trace.

The Lowestoft area bore the brunt of the shipping tragedies but big losses also occurred at many other points along the coast, particularly at Yarmouth, Gorleston and Palling.

Lifeboatmen from every station along the East Anglian coast were engaged in the struggle on that Black Saturday, saving many lives at no little risk to their own. By the time the storm had receded, more than 60 rescued seamen crowded in the Sailors' Home at Lowestoft alone. It was reported that within three miles of the town's harbour at least 16 vessels had been wrecked and some 30 lives lost.

Ruined tower in the Garden of Sleep

"I strolled on and, attracted by a ruined church tower, took a cut through the cornfields towards a cluster of farms and a distant village. It is difficult to convey an idea of the silence of the fields through which I passed, or the beauty of the prospect that surrounded me — a blue sky without a cloud across it, a sea sparkling under a haze of heat, wild flowers in profusion around me, poppies predominating everywhere."

This is a passage from an article that appeared in the *Daily Telegraph* in August 1883. The column was titled *Poppyland* and the writer was Clement Scott. It was the first of a series about North Norfolk which was to change the area to such an extent that Cromer quickly became one of the most fashionable resorts in England.

The tower, at the centre of the story, was sited on the edge of the cliff near the village of Sidestrand. It had been part of St Michael's Church which was moved further inland as it was obvious that cliff erosion would eventually lead to its demise. A service was held in the church on the cliff-top at Christmas 1880 and then, brick by brick, it was moved. The tower, which did not match the rest of the church and barely reached the height of the nave, was left to battle alone with the wind and the waves.

"The Garden of Sleep" was the name Scott, in his writings, gave to the tower and its graveyard. It helped to popularise the area and with it came the development of a Poppyland industry. There were many stories concerning Scott and his love for a miller's daughter as described in this verse of his entitled "A Summer Song".

The ruined tower, in the Garden of Sleep, survived for many more years. One morning, in 1916, the people of Sidestrand saw the tower on the cliff top. At midday two villagers reported that it had gone. Gradually the graveyard slipped away and the bones, sticking out of the cliff were a morbid attraction, along with the stones of the tower on the beach.

In my garden of sleep, where red poppies are spread
I wait for the living, along with the dead!
For a tower in ruins stand guard o'er the deep
At whose feet are green graves of dear women asleep!
Did they love, as I love, when they lived by the sea ?
Did they wait, as I wait, for the days that may be ?
Was it hope or fulfilling, that entered each breast
Ere death gave release and the poppies gave rest ?
O! life of my life ! on the cliffs by the sea
By the graves in the grass I am waiting for thee !

The only spectacular aspect of the winter of 1889 was the hoar frost which occurred early in January as a prelude to more severe weather later. Certainly the countryside bordering the River Gipping on its journey from Needham Market to Ipswich looked picturesque as this photograph shows. The caption accompanying the picture reads: "This scene represents the waters of the river from which our town (Ipswich) derives its name. It is "headed-up" at the position of the old wooden bridge, by which we were wont to traverse from the foot thereof next the towing path into the Handford Road, then for the use of The Handford Oil Mill, now for sewage flushing services. Every branch and twig is coated with lovely crystals of uncommon length and four or five feet of the river on either side is frozen. Long may we have here the sight of the river as it remains, part of which has attracted many an artist."

The Great Cold of 1891

AFTER 21 consecutive days of severe frost, the longest recorded in Norfolk and Suffolk since the early nineteenth century, warmer weather returned on 1st January, 1891— but not for long. The Great Cold continued through January and February and there was skating on The Broads and other lakes and ponds throughout East Anglia.

The *Eastern Evening News* said that, compared with 1881, the winter of 1891 was a more enjoyable affair. The people of Lowestoft got together for a great ice carnival on the North Denes with a list of characters ranging from Dick Turpin to Red Riding Hood. It was estimated that more than 100,000 had been skating on The Broads during the cold spell.

Inevitably there was tragedy. At Stowmarket, two girls aged 13 and 11 were drowned when the ice gave way. During this remarkable winter it was reported that there were 31 degrees of frost in Vienna and in Frankfurt, seven people were frozen to death.

Sheep roasting ceremony on Oulton Broad in January 1891 — another intensely cold year.

Sheep roasting on Oulton Broad

February, 1895

SO cold was the February of 1895 that rivers froze solid, roads were as hard as iron, birds died in their thousands, vegetation suffered and soup kitchens were set up to alleviate the problems of the poor and perishing. The ice on the Thames was so thick that a pair-horse coach laden with passengers was driven along a stretch of it. On the Broads it was even thicker.

It was said of Oulton Broad that the ice that winter measured 10.5 inches and "you could have driven a steam-roller over it". That was never put to the test but thousands of people enjoyed many graceful days of skating as well as the traditional sheep and bullock roasting.

On occasions barbecues took place on the frozen waters of Oulton Broad near to Mr William Everitt's granary. On 11th February, 1895 the thermometer slipped to 0F (-18C) in East Anglia and Britain's coldest ever temperature was attained -17F (-27C) at Braemar in Scotland* On this day ships were welded together in the ice and many people died of exposure.

*This record low of 1895 was equalled in 1982, also at Braemar.

Another — even bigger blow

THE great October gale of 1882 was infamous enough to warrant the name Black Saturday but it cannot compare with the storm in March 1883 when 400 men and boys were lost in the North Sea — and that was just the British losses. The total toll is believed to have been nearer 1,000.

Many of the sailing smacks were caught on the Dogger Bank — that notorious graveyard at sea — where they were knocked down and overwhelmed by mountainous waves. One smack was completely turned over by a huge wave — then righted by the next one — with all her crew gone.

For days after the storm had abated, surviving smacks — many from Lowestoft and Yarmouth — were struggling home and at one time so many were anchored off the Humber, their riding lights looked like a small town.

Storms can strike at any time in the North Sea but November is a particularly treacherous month. There was a vicious storm on 28th November, 1897 with "such a tide as has never been seen before".

That, however, is another story.

One of the most graphic examples of cliff erosion. The garden of a house at Pakefield has slipped into the sea, leaving the flint-built well and its lid, in the shape of a small house, still standing. The date of this photograph taken by Jenkins of Lowestoft, is 1896 and the incident occurred during one of the storms of that year.

BELOW: Walking on the River Deben at Woodbridge during the freezing February of 1895.

A cartload of boys negotiates Belvedere Road, Lowestoft during the notorious floods of 1897.

In what was described as the worst blizzard since 1881, many villages in Norfolk and Suffolk were cut off by drifting snow during the last weekend of January, 1897. Mail drivers and trains were hindered and, at Bury St Edmunds, a man was killed when he attempted to cross the road in the blinding blizzard. He was knocked down and run over by a cart. Seas were also rough and the lifeboat crew at Gorleston, responding to signals from a steamer in distress, were thrown into the sea. All were saved. The crew of the smack, Sultan was not so lucky. A report reached Yarmouth that the boat had been hit by a mountainous wave and all four crew members washed away and drowned. Picture shows a more peaceful scene in Seven Cottage Lane, Rushmere St Andrew, near Ipswich.

Aldeburgh, as always, suffered greatly in the storm of 1897. Houses were battered, bathing huts washed away and shingle piled high on the beach. The name Aldeburgh means "old fort" and defence runs all through its history, particularly against both sea and sea-faring invaders. A Roman site has been lost to the waves so has about half the Tudor town.

Just one foaming seething whirlpool

29th November, 1897

THE early morning greeting of the Norfolk countryman invariably includes some reference to the weather. "Mornin' bor, looks like being a fine day", typifies the profound interest he takes in the vagaries of the elements. The same man also has an elementary way of describing the more infamous depressions which strike the county from time to time. He simply uses the word "black".

So 29th November, 1897 was "Black Monday". It was the day when the tide topped the defences again, making serious breaches in the sea wall, flooding the land and creating thousands of acres of salt marshes. It was the day that trees crashed down, chimney pots and telegraph poles were felled, jetties were washed away and rivers burst their banks. The culprit was a northerly wind which accompanied a furious depression.

This is what the *Norfolk Chronicle* said of "Black Monday": "Those persons who are wile in weather lore shook their heads at the skiey signs on Saturday and foretold that a break-up of the calm was nigh at hand. They were right. On Sunday and again on Monday there swept across Norfolk a terrific storm in which a fall in temperature was accompanied by snow and hail mingled with the rain. The gale was attended with disastrous effects."

In Yarmouth the stalls and shelters on Britannia Pier were broken into pieces and the rails and seating were hurled away like matchwood. The crowning disaster came when the heavy sea stormed the concrete wall and, pouring into the garden, "made one foaming seething whirlpool of soil, sand, flowers, greenery and grass".

In Acle, several roofs were blown off and there was great damage to the church. At Lowestoft, shipping casualties were numerous and there was enormous damage on land caused by the high tide "which was of a volume never before experienced in the history of Lowestoft." At Cromer, the far end of the jetty was blown away and the rear end lifted out of position. At Lynn, the force of the gale sent the sea water from The Wash up the River Ouse. At one point it rose to a height of 30 feet and the town was inundated. At North Walsham, the clerk of the parish council had a narrow escape when a chimney pot fell onto a spot over which he had just passed.

'Yow'd ha thowt we wor all a-goin' to be drownded'

LOCAL newspapers had some sensational material to fill their columns in November 1897 but it was the incursion of the sea upon the land which caused the greatest alarm. The *Norfolk Chronicle* wrote: "Such a storm was calculated to exert a most destructive influence upon the none-too-ample defences which resist the endeavour of the sea.

"Between Winterton and Happisburgh the sand hills have been cut back yet again and the level of the beach lowered by 18 inches. Near Horsey Gap the sea has made two huge breaches. The incursion of the sea is one that can only be met by prompt and scientific action by those whose duty it is to maintain our coast line."

The best description came from a Horsey marshman who said: "If yow'd ha' sin th' sea come in, yow'd ha thowt we wor all a-goin' to be drownded. It come in across th' Warrin for nigh three hours — till th' tide went out, an if it hadn't bin for th' decks bein' pretty nigh empty at th' time, I don't know what would harve happened".

His account which is contained in *Norfolk Broads* by W.A.Dutt blames the Sea Breach Commissioners who employed men at Horsey and Eccles to widen the bases of the sandhills by bringing down more sand from their crests.

"It's their bisness to luke arter th' merrimills, an' if they'd a done it as they should ha' done th' sea 'ud never ha' got thru. Kapin' th' sea out ain't a one-man-an'-a-boy job, as some o' th' commish'ners fare to think it is."

After this disastrous flood, a fund was opened by the mayor of Norwich to help the fishermen and others who had suffered and the inevitable inquiry was held to discuss ways of preventing future encroachments. Not much progress was made. Some years later the county surveyor, a Major Warren, admitted that there was not enough money in the Bank of England to protect the whole of Norfolk from the sea.

High tide at Windsor Road School, Lowestoft on 29th November, 1897.

Aldeburgh loses six brave men

7th December, 1899

AS the long list of casualties at sea mounted in the closing years of the nineteenth century, so the intrepid lifeboatmen of Hunstanton, Wells, Cromer, Yarmouth, Lowestoft, Southwold and Aldeburgh continued to brave the teeth of each tempest in an attempt to save shipwrecked men. Many lifeboatmen lost their own lives.

On 7th December, 1899 the 18-man crew of the Aldeburgh Lifeboat, returning from routine service in mountainous seas, was struck by a heavy curling breaker which fell on the boat broadside and capsized her. Twelve of the crew freed themselves but the other six were imprisoned underneath. The lifeboat drifted ashore where those on land vainly attempted

to raise the heavy boat sufficiently to extricate them or to knock a hole in the bottom of the boat in time to save their lives. Those lost were John Butcher, Thomas Morris, Herbert Downing, Charles Crisp, Walter Ward, James Miller Ward and Alan Easter.

During the ten years prior to this tragedy the Aldeburgh Lifeboat had been one of the busiest in the RNLI. She was launched on 55 occasions and saved a total of 152 lives.

It was by no means an isolated incident. On 29th October 1880, the Wells Lifeboat had capsized when returning to shore after a service launch. Eleven out of her crew of 13 drowned, leaving ten widows and 27 children.

Woodbridge, one of the most attractive towns in Suffolk, suffered badly in the floods of 1897 and again in the December floods of 1904 (see above). The River Deben rises in Debenham in High Suffolk and flows via Wickham Market to Woodbridge where it widens considerably and becomes tidal — so floods are not uncommon. In olden days Woodbridge was a port of considerable trade, sending ships laden with corn to Scotland and Ireland. In 1722, when Daniel Defoe visited the town, it was the chief port for the "shipping off" of Suffolk butter.

CHAPTER THREE: 1900 — 1910

More coast swallowed by the sea

1900: A cold February with much snow at Ipswich was more than compensated for by a July heatwave when the mercury reached 88F (31C) on the 25th.

1901: A very dry year and sunny. Felixstowe recorded 2046 hours of sunshine. An observer at Bury St Edmunds said that the dry months of May, June, July and August were most disastrous for West Suffolk. At Hillington the mercury reached 90F (32C) on 10th August. Land springs were low at Norwich but at Rumburgh it was reported that the wheat crop did well. On the last day of the year the temperature reached 60F (16C) at Great Yarmouth, the highest recorded in Britain on this date.

1902: February was cold with a mean temperature of 34F (1C) at Ipswich. A fierce rainstorm in Ipswich gave 3.25 inches (83mm) in just two hours on 1st July.

1903: Norfolk and Suffolk were on the edge of the great storm that raged in northern Britain on 27th February when the defence works at Kirkley and a large portion of the cliffs were eaten away. The year as a whole was very wet especially in Suffolk and, in the middle of June, 3.69 inches (94mm) fell in one week at Ipswich.

1904: A great contrast to the previous year. Field drains at Halesworth and many water holes were dry. In December a great fog descended on East Anglia resulting in the infamous "Black Christmas". At Little Saxham the fog was thick from 21st to 27th December.

1905: July was a glorious month in another dry year. At Copdock near Ipswich the average maximum temperature was 77F (25C) with 81F reached on 11 days. At Bury St Edmunds it exceeded 71F on all but one day during the month. At Ash Bocking great difficulty was experienced in obtaining a water supply. The vicarage pond, usually nine feet deep, was empty for much of the year.

1906: A year with some outstanding weather events. An active cold front swept south-east across Norfolk and Suffolk on 8th February with widespread thunderstorms and tornadoes. An early warm spell in March sent the temperature up to 67F (19C) on the 7th at Norwich. On 31st August it reached 91F (33C) in the city and, on 3rd September, a scorching 93F at Westley. Christmas brought heavy snow.

1907: A cool year. The warmest conditions were reserved until late September when, on the 25th, the temperature reached 77F (25C) across East Anglia.

1908: A fierce storm on 22nd February came on with great suddenness at 4.30 pm in Norwich. Winds gusted to hurricane force accompanied by stinging squalls of hail. In just 10 minutes there was much damage to buildings and trees. At Yarmouth the anemometer recorded 90mph. On 23rd April there was a great snowstorm with a depth of nine inches at Hethersett. At Bury St Edmunds this snow added to a previous fall and measured 17 inches. The summer was cool but October brought welcome sunshine with 74F (23C) on the 14th at Geldeston.

1909: A year which was described by farmers as having the most disastrous harvest ever. This poor summer was preceded by a May which provided 270 hours of sunshine. June, however, was damp and cold and, on the 27th in the early afternoon the temperature plunged to 48F (9C) and hail was falling.

Launching of the Aldeburgh lifeboat in 1909, a year of blustery weather and numerous "incidents" in the North Sea.

Was the abnormal tide which attacked the whole of the East Anglian coast on 6th January, 1905 any worse than the great tidal surges of Black Monday and Black Saturday? The usual in-depth coverage which newspapers gave to such weather events was certainly missing but the effects of the storm were disastrous.   At Lowestoft, Pakefield, Kessingland and Southwold huge chunks of cliff were scoured away leaving scores of homes standing precariously near the edge. Tidal flooding was bad in Lynn, Norwich and Yarmouth. Fishing boats were carried away at Cromer. Everything built to protect the crumbling coastline had been attacked by the force of the sea. The Lowestoft Journal said the tide was the highest known by the present generation and the collection of houses to the east of Whapload Road was badly flooded. "These for the most part are inhabited by the poorer classes, people who live from hand to mouth, and the influx of water into their dwellings, accompanied by a good deal of filth has been to them a source of considerable hardship. Had it not been for the sea wall on the Denes some of the so-called houses might have collapsed altogether." Photograph shows the scoured seafront at Pakefield.

Damage caused by the high tide in Lowestoft — 7th January, 1905.

North Quay Suspension Bridge at Great Yarmouth after the spring tide of 7th January, 1905.

A tragic example of coastal erosion is provided by these two remarkable pictures of the Cliff Hotel, Pakefield. The first was taken in 1890 and shows a group of people posing in the road outside the hotel. Between them and the sea are more buildings. The second was taken just 16 years later and shows how much the sea has advanced. The cliff edge is right outside the front door of the hotel, which is facing imminent collapse. In his book Suffolk Scene, Julian Tennyson wrote: "Perhaps in a thousand years, perhaps in five hundred, perhaps even in 50....the whole of the Norfolk and Suffolk coast, one of the loveliest in England will have disappeared down the gullet of its original owner who has been hungering after it ever since he disgorged it centuries ago. And ever since that time we have been searching for something to combat his greed. Brains and money, both of which have been used in fair measure, are mighty combinations, but the sea is mightier still".

People could not protect their own properties, nor could the local authorities. So who was going to stop these priceless chunks of England from crashing, every so often, into the sea? The answer came early in 1907 when the Government appointed a Royal Commission to look into, and hopefully arrest, coastal erosion.
These Knights in Shining Armour, in the guise of bowler-hatted senior civil servants, paraded before the photographers on the clifftop at Lowestoft before making their official tour of the vulnerable areas of East Anglia.

The survivor. This was the last house left at Slaughden, near Aldeburgh. It finally went under in 1933.

Edwardians enjoying the beach at Lowestoft. The photograph was probably taken in June or July in the balmy summer of 1906 when temperatures, in September, soared into the eighties and, at Wanstead, Essex reached 95F (35C). The Edwardians, like the Victorians, dressed up to go to the beach, and even children were dressed formally in clothes which must have been hot on sunny days. Parasols, veils and long sleeves all helped to ward off the sun. The sea air was considered very beneficial to health.

Skating on The Mere at Diss in January, 1907. The freezing conditions returned a month after the great Christmas snowfall of 1906.

All those dreams come true! Winter wonderland near Ipswich on Boxing Day morning, 1906

Journey by tram in a Christmas blizzard

December, 1906

FROM all parts of the country came the same story of the great Christmas blizzard. A polar low caused heavy snow to fall on Christmas Day, 1906 and, by the end of the week, roads were impassable, mail services delayed and many people were found frozen to death.

A contemporary newspaper report stated: "A working man named Clarke, employed at Colman's mustard works in Norwich was found lying dead in the snow. A man whose name could not be ascertained was also found dead on the part of Hollesley Heath, known as Peewit, near Woodbridge. He was lying face downward in the snow."

A vivid description of the state of the roads appeared in the *Eastern Daily Press*: "As one turned from one street to another people were slipping and slithering; some sitting, some already flat on their backs, while others, attempting to assist them to their feet joined them on the ground, a phenomenon caused by melting snow freezing overnight.

"The Norwich tram drivers were men of resilience. Completely in the open they were buffeted by the most unpleasant weather that nature could provide as they drove back and forth during their daily stint. Those on the top deck shared, with the driver, the hazards of the weather, and of paying for the privilege. The wooden seats were soaking wet, so the passengers stood gripping an iron rail, shoulders hunched, heads down, holding their hats as they swayed with the rocking tram. Above them electric sparks sizzled and spat from a wheel that picked up a current from the overhead wire."

Another irresistible Edwardian beach scene, this time at Southwold. In 1908, August Bank Holiday was one of the hottest and sunniest ever known.

Spring morning with a foot of snow

24th April, 1908

APRIL in East Anglia can be an idyllic month and the April of 1908 was no exception. The month opened with the sun shining and daffodils in profusion. Within days, the cuckoo had arrived. By the 24th April he must have been wondering why he was there. A blizzard was blowing fiercely, trees were lying across the roads, buses and cars were slithering, vessels at sea were in dire trouble and East Anglia was covered by a foot of snow.

The *East Anglian Daily Times* said that "no-one was prepared for the heavy fall of snow which greeted St George's Day. The scene on Thursday night was a typical winter one and facetious Christmas greetings were heard in Ipswich while the snowstorm was at its height".

Later in the year, August Bank Holiday was so hot that record numbers of visitors flocked to the east coast beaches.

Newmarket in April, 1908. One of the casualties was the prestige Babraham Plate race, halted by the snowstorm.

In the handsome avenue leading from the Norwich gates to the front door of Sandringham House, almost all the grand old elms and limes were blown down. The King visited the park to inspect the damage.

Sandringham suffers in furious gale

22nd February, 1908

THE great parks of North Norfolk — Blickling, Felbrigg, Sheringham, Holkham and Sandringham — suffered terrible damage on Saturday 22nd February, 1908. Long avenues of trees were laid low in a gale which sprang from the south-west and, in some places, was almost cyclonic. There were violent flashes of lightning and lives lost on sea and land.

Buildings also suffered, particularly in Burnham, Lyng, Stalham, Pulham, Deopham, Diss and Hackford. At East Dereham, the maltings of Messrs Whitbread and Co were so badly damaged that it was estimated the repair bill would exceed £200. At King's Lynn, the corrugated iron roof of the pavilion of the East Gates Bowling Club was carried over the old town wall and the Gaywood River and lodged on the roof of a house on the Spread Eagle Estate.

At Tilney Fen End, a farmer, Mr Isaac Stacey was killed when a post mill was struck by lightning and collapsed on top of him. His son was thrown clear of the falling debris. At Bungay, the cemetery chapel was almost demolished. In Whitlingham, an old man named George Fox employed at the Corporation Farm, was in a shed looking after bullocks when it was struck by lightning. Both George and the bullocks were badly hurt — he was conveyed to hospital, they were destroyed.

CHAPTER FOUR: 1910 — 1919

Unrest on the weather front

1910: A wet year, especially in the Beccles area, with 20 per cent above average rainfall. December was particularly wet and high tides at King's Lynn prevented the opening of the sluice gates. There was heavy material loss on The Fens. On 14th February there was an enormous landslip at Overstrand. A violent thunderstorm in Norwich on 2nd July led to lightning striking the Cathedral spire which put the organ out of action and caused much consternation among a terrified congregation. The New Britannia Pier was opened at Great Yarmouth in July.

1911: A remarkable summer that broke many records, none more so than the 97F (36C) on 9th August at Hillington, near Dersingham which remains as Norfolk's highest value ever. Ipswich measured 1,942 hours of sunshine during the year but drought and heat made for the worst hay crop in 70 years. At Swaffham, from 30th June to 20th August, less than half an inch of rain was recorded.

1912: There were gales at sea in January which culminated in a violent storm on 17th. In mountainous seas, a Dutch schooner, *Voorwaarts* of Groningen sent out an SOS. On this occasion the news was good. The Southwold Lifeboat rescued all five hands and the crew were rewarded with medals and certificates given by the Queen of Holland.

The heat and drought of the previous year were matched by unprecedented rains during August, culminating in the great Norwich Floods when the equivalent of half a year's rain fell. Another drama occurred at sea on 26th August when Coxswain Harris and his crew of the Yarmouth Lifeboat rescued 33 persons from the *Egyptian* in a north-west wind of hurricane force. At Sudbury, on 13th July, a violent hailstorm laid waste whole fields of crops and some of the stones were two inches in diameter. In contrast, December was unusually warm with only one air frost. At Kenninghall, between Diss and Attleborough, spring flowers bloomed in the gardens.

1913: The mild weather at the beginning of the year meant that, by the end of February, some spring flowers were already on the wane. However, winter made a late appearance on 11th April with the currant and plum blossom at Hethersett covered in five inches of frozen snow. At Hingham, shrubs were laden to the ground.

1914: February was remarkably sunny, having only seven hours less sunshine than the previous July. Another feature of note was the appallingly wet December which measured 6.82 inches (174mm) at Aylsham. On 28th December there was a severe gale with many trees damaged at Rendlesham, Suffolk.

1915: The Brandon River burst its banks on 1st January and there was serious flooding at Hockwold and Southery Fen. A brief burst of tropical heat sent temperatures soaring to 90F (32C) on 8th June. Later in the month, violent storms broke out in a number of places. In Norwich, inch long shards of ice showered down and, on 30th June, Mildenhall experienced almost continuous lightning and 2.63 inches (67mm) of rain in 50 minutes.

1916: A wet year lacking in sun with February and March extremely unsettled and snowy. On 28th March there was a heavy snowstorm and many vessels were lost at sea. Two days, later the Zeppelin raids on East Anglia began, killing 43. Overall, during 1916, sunshine amounted to just 1,304 hours, a deficiency of 259 hours. The week before midsummer was similar in temperature to the first week in January.

1917: A cold winter which continued to the third week of April when there was hardly any sign of spring. On 2nd April the temperature at ground level fell to 6F (-14C) and an air minimum of 17F (-8C) with frosts every night to the 18th in Norwich. There was a burst of extreme heat in June when 93F (34C) was recorded at Little Massingham. July was wet and it was during this month that Britons, fighting the Third Battle of Ypres on the other side of the Channel became bogged down in the Flanders mud. The year ended with a white Christmas.

1918: The cold of December carried on to the first half of January when the mercury failed to rise above 26F (-3C). Milder weather replaced the chill for the rest of the winter. The old saying that our summer "consists of three fine days and a thunderstorm" did not come true in August when there were three brilliantly hot days with temperatures in the nineties, and then some quieter days.

1919: On 30th January, *SS Nimrod*, Sir Eric Shackleton's Antarctic ship was wrecked on the Barber Sand, off Yarmouth, with the loss of 10 lives. The highest reading of the year was reserved for 11th September with 88F (31C) but the rest of the autumn was chilly with frequent frosts. Overall, the year was one of the coldest this century.

Billowing sails on Oulton Broads. The summer of 1911 was one of the hottest of the century.

Big Heat — and the death-rate soars

The summer of 1911

A RECORD-breaking heatwave with temperatures up to 97F (36C) made the summer of 1911 one of the most exceptional in East Anglia for many years. May and June enjoyed some warm days but July and August were outstanding. Day after day the sun bore down from a cloudless sky onto a parched earth. People, and plants, wilted in the torrid heat; there was a mass exodus to the seaside and thousands of passengers left London in the first week of August for The Broads, Lowestoft, Felixstowe and Yarmouth, where the new Britannia Pier was celebrating its first birthday. The temperature set Britain's death-rate soaring and, with a mortality rate of 19 per 1,000, London was one of the most unhealthy cities in the world.

It was not only people who died in this extraordinary heatwave. Cattle perished for lack of water, food had to be thrown away, people walked on the shady side of the street and crops suffered in the drought. Many Norfolk people plumped for the cooler climes of Canada and, in mid-summer 268 emigrants sailed to Ontario.

There was splendid weather for the coronation of George V on 22nd June, an event celebrated throughout the country with pageants, processions, bonfires and firework displays. The summer of 1911 also saw riots and strikes in many major cities as the fear of widespread famine set in.

It was the great heat, however, which the people remembered best. By early August the temperature had soared into the nineties and on 9th August, at Canterbury in Kent and Epsom, Surrey a sweltering 98F (37C) was recorded which was, until 1990, the highest reading Britain has ever registered. On this day a temperature of 97F was measured at Hillington, which still remains Norfolk's highest value. Inland the heat caused many fires including one that raged for many hours at Jewsons timber yard in Lowestoft.

The big heat came to an end with a severe gale on 1st October which caused immense damage to fishing fleets with many lives lost. A Yarmouth lugger went down with all hands on board. But the weather pendulum swung again. November and December were wet and much of East Anglia endured a soaking with up to 10 inches (250mm) of rain. Almost inevitably there were floods throughout the region.

This delightful picture of children bathing in the sea at Felixstowe was taken at a time when the holiday trade was beginning to flourish. Every coastal town in Norfolk and Suffolk competed for a share in the "sunshine market" and Felixstowe, facing south, was as popular as anywhere.

The resort developed in the Edwardian years. A 20-foot wide concrete promenade was started in 1902 and eventually reached two miles from Cobbolds Point to Manor House. In 1904 a pier was built, half mile out to sea with an electric tram and shelters for the fishermen. From the end Belle steamers took passengers to Yarmouth, Walton-on-the-Naze and even London.

The Victorians and then the Edwardians flocked to Felixstowe in their thousands in search of that well-advertised east coast sunshine. By 1911, when the sun beat down relentlessly for more than 10 hours a day in July and August, this fashionable resort boasted grand hotels and theatres, letting houses and landladies, bathing huts and amusement arcades. But it was the sea and the sand that the little ones enjoyed.

The week that Norwich sank

26th August — 1st September, 1912

THERE could hardly be two more dissimilar months in all the history of weather than that of August 1911 and August 1912. The former was of almost unrelenting sun with drought that turned meadows into deserts and bathed the countryside in shimmering heat hazes as the temperature touched 97F (36C), then a county record for Norfolk.

A year later the August skies were leaden, the air cold and, at Norwich, the rainfall totalled 11.27 inches (288mm), virtually half a year's fall in one month with an unprecedented deluge on the 26th which resulted in the city's most devastating flooding ever remembered. At Blundall, 8.09 inches (207 mm) fell in 48 hours with around 7.5 inches in Norwich as an area of low pressure sat off-shore.

Scarcely a town, village or hamlet was spared. The harvest was destroyed, thousands of people were washed from their homes and the city of Norwich became isolated from the outside world.

Rain commenced early on Monday morning, 26th August, and continued in a prolonged cascade until after midnight. It was accompanied by frightening squalls which brought down hundreds of trees. Millions of tons of water fell on higher ground to the west and north of the city, which then descended in pent up fury through the streets as the Wensum was transformed into a wild, destructive fast-flowing river.

Buildings collapsed. The printing works of the *Norwich Mercury* at St George's had the whole of the front of two lower storeys torn away. On the opposite side of the river another building tumbled and the gable end of the Boston Blacking Company fell into the river.

The side of a house in Churchill Road toppled. Inside, Mrs Meadows scarcely had time to draw breath and recover when the front of the house gave way. The roof held and she was spared injury. The bridges at Trowse and Lakenham suffered a similar fate as did the Ostrich Public House at Kettshill. Although supports had been put up to protect the building, the entire front collapsed and an adjoining cottage was completely wrecked. It happened at 11 pm on Thursday night when many patrons were still about. No-one was injured.

It was estimated that damage in Norwich alone amounted to £100,000 and 15,000 lost their homes or property, 3,650 buildings being damaged or destroyed. Street after street was inundated and, along them, floated a succession of barrels, tubs and palings and a myriad of other items from a host of yards and factories. Through the seething waters one boatman performed heroic rescues, saving in all 100 souls. At one point he was feared drowned when his boat capsized and he tumbled into the swirling floods. He managed to scramble to safety.

Not everyone was so lucky. One rescuer lost his foothold at Bullard Wharf and was swept away. A policeman and an ex-member of Parliament, Mr Tillet, carried two nurses on their shoulders for 50 yards, scaled two brick walls and finally succeeded in heaving them through a window so they could help deliver a baby.

All over Norwich boats plied the streets. One carrying 18 to 20 women and children struck spikes and began to sink rapidly. Another came to the rescue — just in time.

Away from the city, Broadland was devastated. What should have been the height of the season with sails billowing was lost. The rising flood waters carried sediments which silted up the waterways and had a serious effect on the boating and waterborne industries.

Roads and railways were impassable in all directions. One lady, travelling to North Walsham from North Elmdale, began her journey at 2.45 pm on Monday. Her train was diverted to Kings Lynn, then Newmarket, Ely, Cambridge, even Liverpool Street and onto Yarmouth. She eventually reached her destination at 4.10 pm the following day — and the last part had to be completed by road. In another incident hundreds of passengers were marooned at Yarmouth railway station. The station master lit fires in the waiting rooms and allowed people to sleep in the carriages.

Back in the city, a massive relief operation was necessary for the thousands of men, women and children rendered homeless. Seven schools were opened for refugees who were made as comfortable as possible. Hundreds of blankets were provided and those who remained in their homes were visited by relief parties in boats who distributed essential foodstuffs.

Many workers lost their tools in the water and were effectively unemployed for several weeks while factories repaired storm and flood damage. As the waters receded there were many poignant scenes but the most bizarre was the sight of a piano in Lothian Street suspended on its back across four chairs with water dripping out of the keys.

The bridge crossing the river between Forncett and Flordon was washed away leaving the railway line dramatically suspended in the air.

The city of Norwich was blacked out. Little wonder, for the Electricity Works were flooded.

Horses and carts convey people to safety as the flood waters rise.

To the rescue. The city's fire brigade begin to pump out gallons of water.

Office workers and shopkeepers help police with the rescue work.

Posing for the camera in Magdalen Street

A rowing boat in Norwich city centre with all your mates. For the younger children it was fun!

A watery meeting place for the children and (right) bread for the hungry.

The Norwich Floods. Handing a loaf to a flooded-out cottager.

COPYRIGHT L.N.A. PHOTO.

The floods at Framlingham in 1912.

Brandon, Suffolk snowbound in February, 1916. Soldiers can be seen in the distance, marching towards their two colleagues.

THE FLOODS. SOUTHERY. NO 63 PHOTO RABY.

A house at Southery, near Downham Market, badly damaged in the floods of 1916

The siege of Southery Fen

14th March, 1916

MARCH, 1916 was snowy and wet. Day after day, rain poured down from a leaden sky and, on 13 days, when it was too cold for rain, there were squally blizzards. By the end of the month swollen rivers were threatening to burst their banks. Suffolk and Norfolk, and in particular, those living in the vulnerable fens, were praying that the crisis would pass.

On 28th March the "worst blizzard for 35 years" raged across East Anglia. The *Norfolk Chronicle* said that "very few people can recall such a storm as that experienced on Tuesday night and, owing to a complete breakdown in telegraph and telephone communications, it is not possible to give our readers but very scant news."

At East Dereham, fallen trees blocked roads and railways. As Dereham was an important postal centre for the eastern counties, the blockade brought the whole service to grief. "Motor mail vans from Blakeney and Fakenham did not arrive", said the Chronicle, "and it was only late on Wednesday that their whereabouts was discovered".

As usual, it was Fenland which really suffered. The river levels, supplemented by the falling snow rose higher and higher until they were unable to cope with the sheer weight and speed of the water. Defences capitulated and swirling brown floods rushed through hamlets and villages, embracing everything in their reach. The area around Wereham, Denver, Hilgay, Fordham, Brandon Creek, Feltwell and Hockwold was inundated. People were trapped, trees and shrubs were torn from the ground and farm animals drowned. At Southery Fen, the damage was vast. A huge lake spread as far as the eye could see. Buildings were damaged, roads and rail lines completely submerged and dozens of families were forced to escape by whatever means they could.

The bronze bust of Henry Blogg, the most decorated lifeboatman in the history of the service looks out to sea from a vantage point above the town beach at Cromer. Blogg had the most extraordinary introduction to seamanship. The year he left Goldsmith's School on the corner of Overstrand Road to join his stepfather in the crab boat, he saw the Yarmouth pleasure steamer, Victoria, wrecked on top of a church! The ship had struck the remains of Shipden Church and was badly holed. The passengers were rescued and sent home by train. The young Blogg, then 12, dreamed of joining the lifeboat service but it was six more years before he became a member of the crew.

Henry Blogg and his mighty men

9th January, 1917

A Swedish steamer, *Fernebo* was battling in heavy seas during a terrific gale off the North Norfolk coast on 9th January, 1917 when she struck a mine and was blown in half. Distress signals went out immediately to the Cromer Lifeboat station but the lifeboatmen were already in the North Sea attempting to rescue the crew of a Greek steamer, *Pyrin*. They had been out for several hours; the men were physically sick and mentally drained and it was unlikely that they could summon the energy to relaunch the boat on return.

Coxswain Henry George Blogg, an outstanding figure in the history of Cromer, had other thoughts. Having rescued the 16 Greek seamen, Blogg and his crew somehow launched once more and spent many more hours on the turbulent seas searching for the *Fernebo* and her tragic crew. There was no sign of the wreck but the lifeboatmen refused to give up. Their tenacity and endurance were finally rewarded — the *Fernebo* was spotted and 17 were saved from a certain watery grave.

For this action on those mountainous seas, alive with numerous mines, Henry Blogg was awarded the RNLI gold medal, William Davie and Stewart Holmes won the silver medal and a bronze went to 12 other members of the Cromer lifeboat for their "high degree of physical endurance, unwavering courage and skilful seamanship." "If any one of these qualities had been lacking", said the citation, "the crew of the wrecked vessel could not have been saved."

Henry Blogg had joined the Cromer crew in 1894 at the age of 18 and taken over as Coxswain in 1909 — a job he was destined to hold for another 38 years. During his 50 plus years as a lifeboatman, the Cromer lifeboat was launched 387 times and rescued 873 lives.

Blogg's record was without equal in the history of the Institution. He won the gold medal, which is only given for conspicuous gallantry, three times. He won its silver medal, four times. He held the George Cross and the British Empire Medal. He died in 1954, aged 78.

CHAPTER FIVE 1920 — 1929

The roaring twenties

1921: A year of almost unrelenting drought, the driest back to 1727 and the start of rainfall records. At Felixstowe, only 11.26 inches (288mm) fell, less than 60 per cent of average. A rare wet day produced a deluge at Orford on 11th September with 3.44 inches (88mm) or 21 per cent of the year's rainfall. Severe cyclonic gale on 6th November across East Anglia. Norweigian steamer, *Alf*, sank off Lowestoft with the loss of 16 seamen.

1922: The summer was all rolled into May with temperatures reaching 89F (31.7C) in Norwich on the 20th. June, July and August were cool and wet, a complete contrast to the previous summer. Heavy rainfall in Norfolk on 14th July produced 2.70 inches (69mm) at Fakenham in 24 hours.

1923: "Do not cast a clout 'till May be out" was an appropriate weather saying for this year. Temperatures reached 82F (28C) in places on the 4th May, hail fell on the 16th and it was below freezing on the 24th. July was hot and, by the 11th, the mercury had climbed into the 90's on the Fahrenheit scale. November was cold and December brought a white Christmas to Norfolk.

1924: A year with little in excess of rainfall, temperature and sunshine. December ended with the soil temperature some 7.5F (4.2C) higher than the previous year.

1925: An old Scandinavian saying runs...."As the days lengthen, the cold strengthens." This was true of 1925. January was mild but March brought eight days of snow and frost was on the ground for 25 days. A block at Gorleston Isolation Hospital was struck by lightning on 9th May and destroyed.

1926: The weather was kind to the public holidays. Temperatures reached 75F (24C) on Easter Sunday (4th April). Whitsun was warm and sunny and the August Bank Holiday produced 12 to 13 hours of sunshine on each day. The warmest day of the year was reserved for 19th September with 86.3F (30.2C) in the Norwich area.

1927: A wet year with almost 36 inches (919mm) at Aylsham and Cromer. Henry Blogg of Cromer Lifeboat Station received a bar to his Lifeboat VC on 28th March. There was an extensive fall of cliff at Cromer on 28th August. Another big cliff fall at Trimingham on 6th October. There was a late burst of warmth in early November with 67F (19.4C) at Geldeston on the 2nd. December brought a cold wave culminating in a great Christmas snowstorm.

1928: A violent thunderstorm caused widespread power cuts on 11th February. A thick snowfall, five inches deep covered north Norfolk during the second week of March, but sunny weather followed.

1929: A bitterly cold February as a mighty area of high pressure settled down across Europe. It was one of the coldest on record with seven days in a row below freezing. March brought a rapid rise of temperature, as high as 67F (19.4C) on the 10th. The month was dry and completely rainless at Bury St Edmunds. The last three months of the year were very wet. At Wymondham, more rain fell during those months than the rest of the year put together.

The "desert year" of 1921

A wedge of high pressure which stretched north-east from the Azores towards southern England and refused to budge for several months, brought to Norfolk and Suffolk the lowest annual rainfall since the eighteenth century. This was 1921, better known as the "desert year" when less than 12 inches (300mm) of rain fell on the two counties and had a remarkable effect on both animal and vegetable life.

The summer months were memorable. June was almost rainless in places and by July the countryside was so dry that thousands of fires broke out, particularly on farms and embankments, straining the resources of the firemen. People thronged to the seaside, hotels were full and beaches packed with sun-worshippers, many well protected from the hot rays. In Norfolk, on 10th July, the temperature reached 90.2F(32C).

East coast fishermen were not so happy, for they remembered 1921 as the most disastrous season on record. No herrings were taken until after the second week in September and most crews finished in debt. Even the worms were driven so far into the ground as to make their capture both laborious and, at 5s for 120 of them, very expensive.

Unlike 1911, when there was widespread disease, 1921 was healthy and the death rate for East Anglia was the lowest on record.

Norwich's particular association with thunderstorms of tropical intensity continued in June, 1926 with a downpour that brought half an inch of rain in five minutes and rattling hailstones which ruined crops and devastated gardens.

The Eastern Daily Press said the storm "was memorable as an extraordinary prelude to the longest day when the sudden intensity of the tempest produced hailstones like marbles".

Recounting the trail of damage across East Anglia, the newspaper said "some old timers may recall bygone storms such as the August rainfall of 1912, the disastrous flood of 1878 and the tremendous visitation of August, 1843."

A "venerable 95-year-old" wrote to the newspaper, describing the latter storm as the most terrible of all. He was a schoolboy at the time living at Bracondale.

Photograph shows a modern car of the day battling through flood water at Blythburgh.

Two nights and a day in a north-east gale

THE outstanding service of 1922 and one of the finest in the annals of the Royal National Lifeboat Institution was carried out on 21st October, 1922 by the Lowestoft motor lifeboat and the Gorleston pulling and sailing lifeboat, after a struggle lasting two nights and a day in a fierce north-east gale.

In these heavy seas, the SS Hopelyn from Newcastle was being battered to pieces on North Scroby Sands and a successful rescue looked almost impossible. Hour after hour the lifeboatmen stuck to their task and, eventually, the whole crew of 24 was safely brought ashore.

A gold medal was awarded to Coxswain William Fleming of Gorleston and bronze medals to each of the other 15 members of his crew. For the Lowestoft men there was a gold medal to Coxswain John Swan, who was aged 70 at the time, silver medal to motor mechanic R. Scott and bronze to the eight crew. Commodore E.S. Carver, divisional inspector also received a silver medal.

The Lowestoft Lifeboat Station is among the oldest in the British Isles and this gallant joint rescue with Gorleston was one of the most celebrated of all.

A rival to the greatest blizzard

December, 1927—January, 1928

RAIN on Christmas Day, 1927 turned into snow just after dark. The snow turned into a blizzard. The blizzard raged all night — and by the next morning roads were hopelessly blocked, trains snowbound, vehicles buried and villages marooned. Gales lashed the east coast. Without a doubt this was a blizzard to rival the greatest of the nineteenth century. It was followed, in early January, 1928 by a thaw. The thaw was accompanied by heavy rain and, anxious to get in on the act, the North Sea produced a tidal surge which caused more damage to the Norfolk and Suffolk coast. Then, to cap it all, there were floods.

The weather in December had given no indication of the historic events to follow. It was dry and cold up to 22nd December then, on Christmas Day, a fairly deep area of low pressure moved from the Atlantic to the Channel and across France. At the same time cold north-east winds were brought back into contact with warm southerlies.

Christmas Day was miserable with lashing rain and sleet in places. As the wind strengthened to gale force, huge snowflakes began to fall giving weather "that was wilder than any experienced in East Anglia since the memorable blizzard of 1881".

By Monday 29th December, a single path on most main roads in the two counties had been cleared for traffic but all the others were blocked by snow. Communities right across Norfolk and Suffolk were isolated for more than a week. Letters piled up in the main post offices, traders suffered from lack of business and, in many villages, beer supplies ran dry. Help, though, was always on hand. At Woodditton in Suffolk, it took ten men a day and a half to dig their way through the drifts.

A reporter from the *Eastern Daily Press* who made a first hand investigation in the neighbourhood of Swaffham wrote: "It was impossible to get to Watton from Swaffham for the single track ended in three feet of snow. All communication with King's Lynn was cut off but I saw gangs of men and snowploughs busy clearing the roads."

Commenting on the height of the drifts, the reporter said: "Without exaggeration I can honestly say that I saw drifts from eight to ten feet deep, and these on a main road. They were banked in all kinds of shapes for miles and miles along the road. The spectacle was unique and wonderful."

There was little to wonder at sea. On Boxing Day morning, the Cromer Lifeboat was launched in the teeth of the gale to go to the assistance of a steamer flying distress signals near the Dudgeon lightship. By 9 pm the lifeboat had not returned to Cromer and concern grew for the safety of Coxswain Blogg and his crew.

As the blizzard finally blew itself out, people fought their way through the snow to inspect the damage to the coastline. They found serious erosion to the beach between Corton and Pakefield. They found the mouth of Lowestoft Harbour menaced by the disappearance of the Ballast Groyne which protected the bar from silt. They saw that Gunton and Corton Denes had been flooded and Hunstanton had suffered immense damage. A train from Melton Constable to Yarmouth was stuck in the snow near Corpusty and two engines were sent from Melton to pull it out. They suffered the same fate and all three remained in the snow all night.

On 28th December came news that the Cromer Lifeboat was safe at Grimsby. Coxswain Blogg reported that he and his crew were 12 hours at sea.

The great blizzard prevented many traders getting through with supplies but Mr W. Jackson of Moulton, agent for the Bury Free Press for 33 years, distributed the newspaper as usual in this sturdy car.

They found it impossible in such heavy seas to get back to Cromer or Yarmouth, so they steered to Grimsby. His comment on the drama was a typical Norfolk understatement. "The lifeboat", he said, "stood its test well."

The new year, 1928 brought a sudden change in the weather from frost to thaw. It was accompanied by heavy rain causing rivers to burst their banks and roads, which were impassable a week earlier, became so again. The main Bury to Sudbury road was covered with three feet of water when the River Lark flooded and, at Sicklesmere, a man had a lucky escape when he slipped off the wooden bridge into the river and was carried downstream by the current. The local policeman, Pc Gosling saw the man disappear, jumped into the water and, after a struggle, rescued him. Neither man could swim.

All rivers in the two counties flooded and many people, in more isolated areas, awoke to find themselves surrounded by water. Drivers received a warning from the AA to "keep their engines running at a high rate of revolutions when passing through a flood in order to prevent the exhaust pipe being submerged, and to test their brakes after coming successfully through the water".

In London, the calamity that many had been predicting for years, finally happened. The Thames burst its banks, flooded thousands of acres of low-lying land, drowned 14 people and caused millions of pounds worth of damage. More than 1,600 families needed assistance.

Lightning strikes Cromer Church

THE tower of Cromer parish church was struck by lightning during a severe tempest on 9th November, 1927. It happened at 10.30 pm when townsfolk heard a terrible crash of thunder and then a loud report as if something had exploded. People rushed to the street and saw flames coming from the ground immediately to the west of the south porch of the church. The Fire Brigade extinguished the blaze and discovered that the lightning conductor on the church tower had led the electricity to earth and saved the building. The alarm caused by the storm was considerable. Many fishermen thought the signal had gone for the lifeboat and there was great commotion.

Boxing Day, 1927, after the great snowfall at Exning in West Suffolk. These photographs of his sister were taken by Frank Day of Vine Cottage, North End Road.

When the sea froze at Hunstanton

THE sea around the pier at Hunstanton froze during February 1929, which was one of the coldest of the century. On the 12th and 13th the daytime maximum temperatures in East Anglia were 23F (-5C) and by the 15th it had plunged to within half a degree of zeroF (-17.5C) at grass level.

Snow, several inches deep, carpeted the two counties. The month averaged just below freezing, putting 1929 in fifth place for the coldest February of the century behind 1947, 1986, 1963 and 1956.

Another photograph of Miss Day at Hildersham, near Linton on 31st December, 1927.

Jack Howlett with the shovel, in North End Road, Exning, where the snow was about 10 feet high on 29th December, 1927.

February, 1929 may have been cold but, for the skaters, there was a wonderful bonus — eight successive days of skating on the Broads, lakes and rivers of Norfolk and Suffolk. The photograph above shows the photographer, Christopher Wilson's daughter with members of the Jenkins family at Oulton Broad. Below, Messrs Cobbold, Larking, P.Alston and R.Alston, all of Sudbury, are about to start a race on the River Stour which ended in agony, for P.Alston was hurt in a collision and required surgical attention.

The milk cart stands in a stream that is just a trickle while Bertie Parnell lowers a pail on a rope to catch water. He then fills the milk cans for the cattle. This was the scene at Castle Acre, near the River Nar in West Norfolk in July, 1929 during one of England's most prolonged droughts. A correspondent to the Eastern Daily Press wrote: "There is a pond near my house over which I walked dry shod, casting my mind back to the day when I got into a round wash tub and rowed me across with two sticks. By the river, further down the road, I once saw four pike pulled out in one afternoon. Now I see nothing but a wandering earwig or beetle." The drought of 1929 became a great menace to health and, on 19th July — the 136th rainless day of that year — the Metropolitan Water Board suspended the use of water for gardens and motor cars.

Another photograph, from Castle Acre, near Swaffham, taken by Viola Farley, shows a lady buying water at a penny a pail.

CHAPTER SIX: 1930—1939

Window on the Thirties

1930: A man was killed at Mundesley on 10th March during another cliff fall. His dog was dug out alive. Later in the year, Mr S.W.Mobbs, Lowestoft Borough Surveyor called for a co-ordinating hand to take charge of coast protection. He wrote: "The only remedy is for the protection of the whole coastline to be a national charge under one ministry. Strenuous efforts in this direction have, and are still being made by local authorities but hitherto without the slightest success". 1930 was a typical weather year, bringing a severe gale on 12th January, a heatwave in August, when the temperature reached 89F (32C), and a very wet September with 5.5 inches (140mm) of rain.

1931: Bitter north east winds in early March covered the ground with six inches of snow. There was a violent hailstorm in Southwold on 15th August which caused cattle to stampede. On the beach, sun blinds were perforated and bathers were badly bruised, or lacerated, by giant hailstones.

1932: Not a warm summer overall but a blaze of heat sent temperatures soaring to record levels on 19th August. A reading of 95F (35C) was recorded at Norwich. Bungay also reached the same mark, making it Suffolk's hottest ever day. During the heatwave the £10,000 Floral Hall on Britannia Pier at Yarmouth was destroyed by fire.

1933: A gale off East Anglia coast on 13th December caused five lifeboats to be launched to rescue the crew of ships in distress. A three-masted vessel, the *Culmore* of Southampton was lost off Aldeburgh with a crew of 12. This was a sunny year and even on 23rd October the temperature stood at 63F (17C). It didn't last. By the 26th a rare mantle of October snow, six inches deep, covered East Anglia.

1934: A warm summer and a December, so mild, that many places in East Anglia failed to record a single frost.

1935: Six degrees of frost on 17th May caused great damage to fruit crops in Norfolk and Suffolk. During the year 1,877 hours of sunshine were logged in Lowestoft making it one of the sunniest resorts in England — just ahead of Yarmouth, Cromer and Hunstanton. September was a wild month.

1936: Spring was well on the way in March with temperatures in the low sixties Fahrenheit. A huge cliff fall at Pakefield on 16th October endangered many houses. There was another cliff fall at Sidestrand on the same day — the village's 29th of the century. Nine men were drowned when the drifter *Olive Branch* capsized near Corton lightship in a violent gale on 17th November. Three more men were lost from the Lowestoft drifter *Justifier*.

1937: The weather was unkind on 12th May — Coronation Day for George VI. Rain poured down and led to the demise of much bunting. There was also a violent thunderstorm on 21st May. 1.56 inches fell in Norwich in two hours — the heaviest fall of rain since 1912. At Sprowston, 2.11 inches fell.

1938: The evening of 25th January was a night of magic when a brilliant auroral display was seen "in a fashion without parallel in living memory". Spring was dry, August Bank Holiday enjoyed nearly 13 hours of sunshine, November was hot — the mercury shot up to 70F (21C) at Mildenhall — and there was a White Christmas. Snow fell thickly throughout the two counties on 23rd December and on Christmas Day, East Anglia presented a festive picture. It could have been a perfect weather year were it not for the catastrophic floods in February.

1939: There was much flooding in January due to heavy rains and melting snows, and wide areas of country were inundated. Southerly winds brought a burst of high summer to Norfolk in April, with 78F (26C) on the 12th in Cromer. It was Britain's highest reading on this date.

Earth tremor throws people out of bed

There was a nightmarish experience for the people of Great Yarmouth and Lowestoft on 7th June, 1931 when the two towns were violently shaken by an earth tremor. The 'quake struck at 1.30 on a Sunday morning and started with a low rumbling immediately followed by a muffled crash. The severe rocking brought down chimney stacks and threw many out of bed.

The shock had come from the sea — instruments showing that it was centred near Dogger Bank. These were the days before all trawlers were fitted with radio and there were fears that some fishermen may have been overwhelmed out to sea. There was an anxious wait, but all returned safely to harbour.

Night that Horsey was evacuated

13th February, 1938

AS if to prove that the deep concern for the East Anglian seaboard was not unfounded and that defences and repairs should be a national responsibility, mother nature decided to make one of her biggest assaults yet on this beleaguered coastline. On 13th February, 1938, the seas were whipped into a frenzy by a terrific northerly gale which then left a trail of destruction from The Wash to Southwold. Cattle and horses were drowned, houses flooded, sea walls damaged and beach huts wrecked. Inland, too, the gale caused mayhem. A Norwich van driver was killed at Tharston when a tree fell on his vehicle.

It was the small community of Horsey which bore the brunt of this invasion. Bursting over the low-lying coastline between Winterton and Palling, a tidal wave made the biggest coastal breach for 50 years and flooded 15 square miles of farms and marshes. Horsey was swiftly surrounded by the sea and its occupants had to be evacuated. Many villagers knew nothing of the oncoming waves until they found the sea within a few yards of their homes. In the darkness it suddenly rushed in, trapping vehicles on the main coast road.

Julian Tennyson was one who saw the effects of the now-historic Horsey breach. "I not only saw the six miles of sea water, but something worse — the tragedy and destruction scattered in the wake of it. The finest fields in Norfolk pitifully wasted, cottages gutted and abandoned, great heaps of rotting fish, windmills peeping absurdly from some still aggravated portion of the flood, farms and their buildings doomed as surely as if the dreaded mark of the plague had been written on their doors.

"And I saw, too, that chasm of a gap in the sea wall. Oh! they worked at it all right, when it was too late. All day, all night, with sand, turf, wood, concrete piles — anything to close the breach, while they prayed for the north-west gale to die away before moon and tide should reach the full. And two nights later the gale rose to hell-bent force; the sea, driven down the Straits of Dover, found no passage there, and came roaring back to vent its rage on Horsey. Down went those wretched bulwarks like wheat before a giant's reaper and in rushed the full torrent of flood.

"So it went on, time after time, while reinforcements from all over the county hurled their strength into that fight of desperate and useless agony, and the deserted village of Horsey cried for mercy from the insatiate plunderer."

The storming sea made inroads right down the coast. Minsmere marshes were transformed into a huge lake that lapped the edges of the woods on Westleton Heath, with many feet of salt water which killed every living thing that could not get out of its way. Parts of Aldeburgh were overwhelmed. The sea washed over the High Street, obliterated the road to Slaughden Quay and destroyed the lonely brick house on the shore, where "Bob the fisherman was born".

The sea wall held at Aldeburgh, but not at Iken. The marsh, stretching up to Snape bridge became a brown, filthy swamp with a muddy morass of oily pools. Southwold was a perfect island, stranded by the flooding of the Blyth behind and below and the onslaught of the sea to the north.

Lowestoft escaped lightly but the sea came over the old wall and flooded the low-lying beach district. Hamilton Road was flooded to its entire length. Occupants piled furniture onto tables and retreated to their bedrooms. At Pakefield, thousands more tons of cliff were lost and two unoccupied houses in Cliff Road tottered and fell into the sea.

The Lowestoft Journal said: "People who had gathered on the cliffs in the moonlight were witnesses of this remarkable scene and some idea of the latest 'bit of England' to be swallowed by the waves is indicated by the fact that on Saturday morning it was possible to cycle in front of these houses."

Watchers kept a vigil on the cliffs throughout Saturday night. When one of the houses crashed into the sea, the gas and water pipes connected to adjoining houses snapped. Workmen were summoned to plug the pipes as gas and water simultaneously escaped. Mr S.Turner of 15 Pakefield Street had an amazing piece of luck. "I looked over the cliff at the end of my garden when I felt the wall move. I jumped back and the wall and area where I had been standing plunged 40 feet into the sea."

It was Horsey which provided most of the action on this Saturday night. The sea came in at a speed which villagers estimated to be two miles an hour. A young milkman, Roy Randell, was marooned for 18 hours on top of a motor car on the Yarmouth-Horsey road which was flooded to a depth of six feet. In the moonlight, boats were sent to the Horsey homes and scores of families were taken to Palling and then to temporary accommodation. By Sunday, it was impossible to get within three miles of the village except by boat. All day the evacuation went on.

Inland, thousands of acres of Fenland were threatened when a serious slip occurred in the river bank near Denver Sluice. In an all-night fight, 300 volunteers saved the surrounding countryside from disastrous flooding.

East Norfolk River Catchment Board met a few days later to assess the damage, which they estimated to be about £13,000 at Horsey, where the breach was 700 yards wide. The Board promised to make efforts to secure a Government grant.

Southwold was a perfect island, stranded by the flooding of the River Blyth and the sea. The bus can go no further.

The wall held at Aldeburgh but the sea washed over the High Street, inundated many shops and houses, obliterated the road to Slaughden Quay and destroyed one brick house on the sea front. Photograph shows some of the villagers inspecting the damage caused by the 1938 breach.

River, broad and dyke is no more....the sea has claimed them all

"Desolation, tragedy — possibly even ruin for the hardworking men of East Norfolk", wrote the *Norfolk Chronicle*, in telling their story of the Horsey breach. "History has repeated itself yet again. But 1897 and 1905 were nothing like the disaster on Saturday night. Looking down the flooded land from the high road between Martham and Somerton one looks on an area of the sea stretching far away into the distance, with here and there a clump of trees or a stack of marsh hay to relieve the expanse of water. River, broad and dyke, through which the leisurely yacht and assertive motor cruiser wend their way in summer, is no more. The sea has claimed all.

"Horsey, the picturesque little village at the end of Horsey Mere has borne the brunt of this invasion. The sea sweeps through the village street, invading farm and cottage alike.

"If the holidaymaker could see this area he would not recognise the watery waste. When he comes in a few months' time the waters will be gone and he will cruise over the placid Horsey Mere, down Meadow Dyke, wend his way across Heigham Sounds and down Kendal Dyke. Now it's a raging flood but in summer there will be a difference; fish will be absent for they have perished, bird life may be altered, plants have suffered from salt water.

"Nature will salve her wounds and in years to come the tragedy of 13th February, 1938 will be forgotten — but not by all."

This photograph was taken from a boat near Waxham after the sea had poured through Horsey.

White Christmas for the young princesses

Hundreds of people battled through heavy snow to greet King George V1 and the royal family as they arrived at Sandringham parish church for the Christmas Day service, 1938. It was a very special occasion — a white marble plaque in memory of George V was unveiled.

It was the first white Christmas since 1927 and the onlookers at Sandringham were delighted when the two little princesses, Elizabeth and Margaret decided to walk back home through the parkland over an unbroken carpet of snow with Lady Mary Cambridge.

Elsewhere the news was not so happy. The snow made it "the worst Christmas ever for the Post Office" and, at Cromer, a great fire destroyed Mr L.F. Gee's cycle shop. Football at Carrow Road, Norwich was cancelled, but nobody was unduly concerned. Norwich had suffered "the most disastrous period in the history of the club" and were second from bottom of Division Two of the Football League.

In their review of the year the *Norfolk Chronicle* said that 1938 would be remembered in history as a year of crisis and international disturbance, but also a year in which world war was averted!

Two nights of terror in Ipswich

25th—27th January, 1939

JUST before 9 am on Wednesday morning 26th January, rain began to fall gently around the Gipping Valley area of Suffolk. Gradually it increased in intensity until the skies opened and the rain cascaded down with the energy of a tropical monsoon, hissing and splashing as it landed.

Some hours later those lush valleys, already overburdened by the thawing of the Christmas snow, were lost beneath the water. Some 78,000 acres had received as much as 429 million gallons; fast-flowing flood water that embraced everything within its reach. By Thursday morning, towns, villages, hamlets, farms were inundated, road and rail traffic was dislocated, telephone communications were chaotic — and the people of Ipswich were about to experience one of the most serious natural disasters in their lifetime.

It was in the city where the full force of the Gipping flood spent itself. Thousands of pounds worth of damage was caused; women and children, old men and invalids were marooned without food, water or fires for up to 36 hours. Families were separated and hundreds of working class homes were ruined. No-one had time to prepare for a disaster of this magnitude. It came without warning.

The first sign of danger was on Wednesday evening after a day in which 2.13 inches had fallen. The watershed could cope with no more and water began to pour from high ground in the Whitton area to find a level in the Dales Road district. It then rose rapidly.

The Ipswich Fire Brigade was called to Dales Road and, with help from an ARP trailer, attempted to pump the water away. The flood rushed into Beaconsfield Road and then onto the Yarmouth Road allotments where pigs had to be rescued by policemen. At Washbrook, buses came face to face with a torrent of water and turned back.

At full tide, 3.35 pm, the River Gipping overflowed its banks and made the main Ipswich-London Road impassable. It poured into the Ipswich Electric Supply Station, surrounded Bramford Village School where children and teachers were marooned and built up to a depth of four feet. Nearby, the bridge over the River Gipping collapsed and the main water and gas pipes were carried away. The trolley bus service was suspended and, as the water level rose even higher, factories sent their workers home.

Ipswich was now on a full scale emergency and all the services co-operated in a massive rescue operation. In Princes Street the water reached a depth of five feet and gushed into surrounding streets, slopping against doors and windows. Cars were swept away and people trapped in upstairs rooms as the swirling brown waters hurtled on.

People were taken from homes in Cannon Street, Great Gipping Street, Friars Bridge Road. Others, marooned in their bedrooms, implored the police to remove them — but they remained stranded. The speed and strength of the floods made rescue impossible.

One lady with vivid memories of the 1939 floods is Doris Clark, of Cambridge Drive, Ipswich. Her parents moved into a house in Princes Street on the Monday and they were flooded out on the Thursday, never to return. "We opened the front door", said Doris, "and in came the water. With my mother, father and brother I ran upstairs and we were marooned there for two nights. The water actually rose to within three stairs of the top and my mother panicked. We were all taken out. Everything was lost — possessions, furniture, photographs and even our cats. We never lived in that house again".

The *East Anglian Daily Times* reported one death, Mrs Emma Robinson, aged 85, of Martlesham who died a few hours after being found in her flooded room. The newspaper wrote: "Throughout a night of ceaseless terror and misery, the rescue work went on and Friday's dawn broke on the worst floods in living memory.

"The only aspect of cheerfulness was the amazing fortitude and good humour with which people faced their ill-fortune. Families in upper rooms leaned from their bedrooms, joking in philosophical fashion with rescue parties bringing food and water by boat."

Organisations and institutions in Ipswich assisted in finding accommodation for flood victims, a soup kitchen was opened in the city and convoys of Territorial Army lorries and vans took children to school and men and women to work.

Saturday saw the floods gradually subside and the "wan and haggard people whose homes had been ravaged began to salvage their belongings". The *East Anglian Daily Times* told stories of newly-married couples who now had to start all over again to get a home together, of men, women and children huddled six and seven together in one upstairs room and of the poor elderly folk whose homes were ruined beyond repair.

An appeal was opened and during the first week money came in at the rate of £1,000 a day.

Princes Street, the main thoroughfare between Ipswich railway station and the Cornhill became a branch of the River Gipping on the afternoon of 26th January 1939. Motor vehicles are marooned.

The scene in Princes Street, opposite the Marsh Tavern.

Horse power was useful in the Chancery Road/Princes Street area of Ipswich. In fact horses were used to haul motor cars out of trouble.

The ruin of the bridge at Bramford, Suffolk. It had to be replaced by a temporary structure after the damaging floods of January, 1939.

CHAPTER SEVEN: 1940—1949

Cold winters and hot summers

1940: A bitterly cold January with blizzards on the 16th and 26th that drove the snow like smoke into huge drifts. In the Breckland area, on the clear night of the 20th, the mercury fell to 4F (-15C) and the monthly average was only just above 29F (-1.7C). The summer did compensate for the chill of winter and June, especially, was dry and sunny averaging 10 hours a day at Yarmouth.

1941: Another cold January with snow on the ground for 15 days. One of the most outstanding features of the year was the cold May. With increased agricultural output needed for the war effort the last thing anyone wanted was spring frosts. However, the temperature fell to an icy 15F (-9C) at Lynford, near Thetford on 4th May and again on the 11th.

1942: The third successive very cold January in which the average temperature for the month was below freezing in Norwich. April was extremely sunny and from the 9th there were 30 successive rainless days. On 14th June, giant hailstones killed birds in the Stour valley at East Bergholt, but this was followed by a heatwave on 27-28th August. Sprowston, with a thermometer reading of 93F (34C), was the hottest place in Britain that year.

1943: A severe gale swept Norfolk in April with 75mph winds which pounded sea defences. At Yarmouth, the river rose so quickly at Cobholm and Southtown that many residents had the alarming experience of being awakened by water pouring into their homes. Norwich was covered in a great cloud of dust whipped up from its bombed areas. Many gable ends and walls collapsed and builders had to be released from repair work on war damage. Dust storms swept the countryside ruining crops on light land. On 15th June hail, up to 1.5 inches in diameter, fell on Lowestoft.

1944: There was a white Christmas this year but not as a result of snow. East Anglia was cloaked in a silent shroud of thick, freezing fog. At Downham Market, on 27th December, the hoar frost covered trees in a breathtaking filligree of ice. At Cromer, the stillness was briefly shattered by a low, rumbling sound and buildings shook at around 1.35 am. There was no damage from this earth tremor.

1945: The year began with good skating conditions on the Fens. After severe gales on 18th-19th January, very cold air spread across Britain and snow covered the ground for 12 days at Rushmore St Andrew, Ipswich. A number of birds were found frozen to death. The August Bank Holiday, after the rigours of war, was the happiest for six years. The weather celebrated with a violent thunderstorm. Lightning plunged Bury St Edmunds into darkness and Lowestoft had an inch (25mm) of rain.

1946: A burst of warmth after a chilly March gave an early touch of summer throughout East Anglia. At Hunstanton, the temperature reached 78F (26C) on 3rd April and 79F (26C) at Mildenhall on the 4th. On the east coast it was very dry with only 9 mm of rain falling at Gorleston during the month. The summer was unsettled and, at times, thundery. A severe storm battered the area surrounding Shouldham Thorpe, south of King's Lynn. Giant hailstones, the size of tennis balls, penetrated the canvas roof of an army lorry and plunged through roofs of cars. North-facing windows were smashed, an orchard ruined and branches stripped. Whole fields of crops were laid to waste.

1947: A truly memorable year with the coldest February on record, snowstorms, floods and gales in March, and a gust of 98mph at Mildenhall. A blazing summer followed with 92F (33C) at Hunstanton on 2nd June. The warm weather continued right through to 16th September when a reading of 88F (31C) was recorded at Norwich. At Great Yarmouth, rainfall was 8.14 inches (215mm) below average for the year, with sunshine 223 hours above. This was typical of many places in East Anglia.

1948: The winter had been mild but on 20th February the temperatures plunged as bitterly cold air spread from Europe across East Anglia on strong 50 mph winds, causing 22 ships to shelter in the roads off Yarmouth. Snow fell widely. Yet, by 9th March, the temperature was 72F (22C) at Gorleston. The summer that followed was not auspicious, but it did produce one hot spell that gave a reading of 94F (34C) at Mildenhall on 28th July — the warmest spot in Britain for that year.

1949: An intense depression led to furious gales across East Anglia. The sea breached dykes near Brancaster and turned the area into a salt marsh. At King's Lynn, the tide level was the third highest recorded. However, the year was better known for its fine, warm weather. During Easter, the mercury approached 80F (27C) and there were more than 40 hours' sunshine. On a fine May day, a mirage was seen from Hunstanton looking northwards. One observer said he could distinctly see little human figures walking to and fro far out on the sea. A group of beach huts was also visible, one of them of a yellowish colour. The warm weather continued into September, with the heat intensifying and 90F (32C) was recorded at Mildenhall on the 4th.

Great Frost was a secret!

December, 1939 — February, 1940

FOUR months after the outbreak of war, with little sign of any hostilities East Anglia braced itself for a more familiar battle. The weather in January, 1940 — a year destined to be one of the most memorable in British history — was bitterly cold with some snow. But as the days wore on, the cold intensified and, by the middle of January, Norfolk and Suffolk were held in the icy grip of one of the most severe frosts of the century.

Lying snow, blown off fields, caused drifts on country roads that were many feet deep. Rivers and Broads froze, towns and villages were cut off and a piercing north-east wind blew for several weeks. But the Great Frost of 1940 was a secret. All references to the weather were censored for 15 days for fear the information would be useful to the enemy. It didn't really matter — the whole of Europe had returned to these Ice Age conditions!

The frost extended, almost unbroken, from 22nd December to 4th February and the maximum daytime temperature was just 38F (3C) in parts of East Anglia. At Thetford, on 31st December, 1939, 20 degrees of frost were registered. Bury St. Edmunds went even lower. On 20th January, a reading of 3F (-16C) was recorded, making it one of the coldest days Suffolk has ever known.

Some of the most amazing spectacles occurred on 27th January on the road between Horning and Neatishead, described thus by the *Eastern Daily Press*: "The whole countryside was like a rolling sea, with majestic waves in arrested motion. On the windward side of the road the snow had been driven into drifts fully eight feet high. All along the road there were fairytale caves and grottoes. At one point a man stood under a crystallised wave which overhung the road for nearly a third of its width. Compressed by its own weight those tiny crystals in the mass looked as solid as marble."

East Anglia was in chaos. Eastern Counties Omnibus Company had to suspend its services after buses became stranded near Risby and Honington. Cars were lost in drifts near Troston. Eight heavy lorries belonging to Westgate Brewery had to abandon their journeys. The village of Brandon was without gas for a fortnight.. Haverhill, in Suffolk was totally cut off. So were Dereham, Yaxham and Garvestone in Norfolk. Near Mundesley, a bus with 22 passengers was stranded on the road all night.

Another sight which attracted great interest near Bury was the sight of 19 pink-footed geese flying in a perfect V formation. These regular visitors to the Broads had never been seen so far inland.

A bus negotiates floods in Lowestoft in the 1940's

Clear blue skies for the Battle of Britain

ON the evening of 9th July, 1940, Norfolk suffered its first baptism of enemy fire when two low-flying German aircraft bombed Norwich and flattened the engineering works of Boulton and Paul. Twenty seven people died. The bombers had excellent visibility on a warm and sunny evening.

The balmy weather continued for most of the summer, but the home advantage was with the RAF, who flew from their bases in Suffolk and Norfolk. Between June to October there were many days when the skies were cloudless and, on these occasions, the Battle of Britain was fought, and won.

It was in September that the battle reached its zenith. All day, every day, the might of the German Luftwaffe skimmed across the treetops of East Anglia. But the threat was repulsed, and eventually the enemy scurried back to its bases, leaving the countryside littered with the wrecks of aircraft.

In October, Hitler postponed his proposed invasion of Britain.

Chronicle of a long, hard winter

January to March 1947

THE notorious winter of 1947 is still considered one of the worst in memory.

Blizzards, sub zero temperatures and overcast skies brought two months of gloom and hardship to families in Norfolk and Suffolk so soon after the war. Food was scarce and rationed. Coal was in short supply. Homes were often unheated and clothes could only be bought with coupons. To make it more miserable, power cuts blacked out towns and villages for hours at a time. All in all, the weather was a severe blow to the country trying to get back to normal after six disrupted years.

It was also bitterly cold. The ice at Oulton Broad was so thick that cars could be driven over it. When the thaw came, large tracts of Fenland were submerged. Homes were inundated and, at Swaffham Prior Fen, the force of the floodwater was so great, a house collapsed into the muddy torrents.

The winter was a late starter. Snow did not fall until 23rd January but that did not stop the big freeze from continuing through February into March. And when the thaw came it brought new hazards. Some of East Anglia's most destructive floods ever known occurred in March. In addition there was a fearsome gale on 16th March which caused extensive damage.

This is how the winter unfolded.

23rd January: High pressure settled over Scandinavia feeding cold air over most of England. Five degrees of frost (-3C) recorded at Mildenhall.

24th January: An inch of snow lying at West Raynham, Norfolk at dawn, gave little warning of what was to come.

28th January: The temperature at 10 pm in Norwich was 19F (-7C) following severe local snowstorms during the day in the Fakenham, Walsingham, Wells, Stiffkey, Cockthorpe and Binham areas. The main road at Acle was impassable but strong winds blowing off the marshes later cleared the road. Snowploughs were out on the Beccles-Scole Road. The Waveney Valley had two heavy falls and ice formed on the river in parts of Beccles and Bungay. At Thetford, after dark, the moon was shining brightly and four inches of snow which had fallen there during the day glistened in the frosty air.

29th January: Nine inches of level, undrifted snow was lying at Felixstowe as people set out to work. At West Raynham there was five inches on the ground and 22 degrees of frost were recorded at Mildenhall. At Gorleston the day dawned with a biting wind blowing at force five and temperatures close to 24F (-5C). It was colder still at Felixstowe.

30th January: More snow showers overnight. Again dawn was bitterly cold. The wind blew in from the sea at force four while the temperature in the air remained at 24F (-5C).

3rd February: A blizzard was blamed for the death of a man, knocked down by a train at East Runton. Signalman, Hugh McLeod went out into the teeth of the biting winds to clear the snow from the points. He was struck by the train from North Walsham at 10 pm. The train driver reported that visibility at times was nil.

4th February: Dimmer street lamps for Fakenham appeared to save power. Blizzards cut off several North Norfolk villages including Bacton. Mini ice floes were seen over the marshes at Bungay where hundreds of acres were inundated. Roads were blocked by drifts and only 11 out of 85 children were able to get to school at Bacton. The parishes of Walcott and Edingthorpe were badly hit by drifts.

5th February: Snow piled up to a depth of 12 feet at Geldeston near Beccles and traffic was impeded on the Beccles-Bungay road by drifting snow. A woman walking towards Northrepps, Norfolk saw what looked like a bag of coal lying in the snow. She discovered it was the top of a coal lorry, almost completely buried.

8th February: Thousands of workers at East Anglian factories were temporarily out of work due to huge industrial power cuts.

10th February: Norwich Corporation sent out six snowploughs to keep the city roads open. 8,500 cubic yards of snow were cleared.

11th February: The worst snowstorm of the year crippled Norfolk. Roads and railways were completely blocked. Trains were marooned and, for a time, Cromer and Sheringham isolated. At Walsingham, snowdrifts were 12 feet high and thousands of children were unable to get to school. In Norfolk it was one of the coldest days ever known. The maximum temperature in places was just 26F (-3C), only a degree higher than the previous lowest in February, 1929. A level foot of snow fell, the most since 1916. The movement of coal throughout the country was severely hampered by the weather — more than 120 ships and 195,000 tons of coal were unable to leave Tyne and Wear.

12th February: Maximum temperature at Mildenhall was 27F (-3C). West Runton was even colder with 25F (-4C).

18th February: A boat from Cantley ran into the ice near the Berney Arms, Reedham and another collier which had delivered coal to Norwich Power Station also became stuck. A third collier somehow forced a passage through the ice.

21st February: Snowstorms on this Friday night were severe. An ambulance had to be abandoned in waist-deep snow at Bintree. The driver had left Fakenham at 8.15 with a patient for Norwich Hospital. The ambulance was dug out of the snow at Little Ryburgh and twice at Bintree. He delivered his

Many people in East Anglia recall how German prisoners-of-war helped to clear the snow during the winter of 1947. This picture was taken at Hunstanton. There are other memories. A former airman, stationed at RAF Mildenhall, remembers taking off in a Lancaster with the door open and dropping supplies of biscuits to airfields at Skapton and Waddington. The pilot was Group Captain Troughton Smith and their call sign was Greengrocer Able.

patient at 11.15 pm, commenced the homeward journey but snow was so deep at Bintree he had to spend the night in the ambulance. He started walking to Fakenham at 6.30 am. A milk lorry and a car gave him a lift but these, in turn, had to give up.

22nd February: Blizzards in North Norfolk. By now the county had suffered 300 hours of continuous frost. Drifts blocked the railway line between Cromer and Runton. A snowplough and four engines became stuck a mile from Cromer Station and 90 men took several hours to dig them free. The Norwich Road was blocked by an abandoned snowplough and, at Beccles, two fire engines were trapped in drifts en route to a fire at Redisham Hall. A collier had to turn back at Reedham. Soldiers cut a way across fields at Southrepps to enable an Army ambulance from Weybourne to get to Mundesley.

23rd February: Mr C.H. Day, a Lowestoft garage owner, made history by driving his car on Oulton Broad. His son, Charles, rode a motorcycle towing a sledge on which many local people went for a ride.

A stretch of ice 700 yards long in the River Yare at Reedham severed the water route between Norwich and Yarmouth. The city of Norwich experienced its coldest night for seven years after a day in which the temperature rose above freezing point for the first time in a fortnight, albeit for just 30 minutes. German prisoners of war were engaged in snow clearance throughout East Anglia.

24th February: An exceptionally cold dawn temperature of 9F (-13C) recorded at Mildenhall. At last the sun appeared — for nearly six hours at Gorleston.

25th February: Even colder at Mildenhall with 7F (-14C). Then the temperature rose to 33F (1C), a fraction above freezing for the first time in many Arctic-like days.

4th March: The bitterly cold weather was back accompanied by a north-east wind. Maximum temperature struggled to 37F (3C) at Felixstowe and at Fakenham 14 inches of snow was on the ground by 6 pm.

There was flooding in many towns and villages as the snow melted. This is Bridge Street Hadleigh, Suffolk when the River Brett flooded in March, 1947.

6th March: Conditions deteriorated. Freezing all day and night with a force four wind in the evening.

12th March: A thaw was forecast after another week of sub-zero temperatures. The prediction was wrong — snow retured.

14th March: Milder weather at last. The thermometer climbed to the dizzy heights of 48F (9C) at Newmarket and rain added to the melting snow.

15th March: Winter returned to East Anglia with a vengeance. Five inches of snow at Fakenham and one inch at Newmarket.

16th March: A fearful westerly gale caused widespread structural damage just over the border in Cambridgeshire. At Fordham, houses were stripped of their roofs and hardly a home was spared at Soham.

17th March: This topsy turvey winter threw East Anglia into more confusion. The mercury reached 52F (11C) near West Row. The following day produced six hours of sunshine at Barton Mills. Now there was devastating flooding.

19th March: One thousand men were employed to close a breach in the bank of the Little Ouse near Hockwold which was threatening vast areas of Fenland with major flooding. German POWs, airmen and anxious villagers worked at various sites to lessen the damage but 6,000 acres were still inundated. Denver was swamped by the swollen St John's Eau. Southery was at great risk. There were sheets of water over farmland at Magdalen Fen. Near Lakenheath the Little Ouse broke through at Wilton Bridge. The force of the water bursting the banks of the Great Ouse at Little Thetford was so great that two barges were swept out into the Fens. The main railway line to Cambridge was submerged and 2,000 acres of rich farmland at Stretham covered with deep water. In Dalham, the floodwater reached its highest level in living memory. People were evacuated from many places including Moulton.

22nd March: The mild weather continued with a temperature of 55F (13C) at Gorleston.

24th March: Sunny and mild throughout East Anglia. Winter had vanished at last leaving floods and a trail of damage in its wake.

Ice blocks on the River Orwell in January, 1947

EASTERN DAILY PRESS; FEBRUARY 22, 1947

BY ICE FROM BECCLES TO OULTON — AND BACK

Skaters' Trip on The Waveney:
First time Since 1894

For the first time since 1894 a party of skaters yesterday made the trip from Beccles to Oulton on the frozen River Waveney. Owing to a head wind, the need for two detours and a voluntary halt at Burgh St Peter, the journey took them about two and a quarter hours.

The return journey to Beccles was made in an hour and six minutes by six of the party, the seventh returning by bus.

The original party comprised Henry Oxborough, Peter and Roger Seppings, Cyril Allgar and Michael Dodd. It was increased by Noel Holmes and Colin Richardson who had started earlier and had been overtaken.

They said they found the ice good all the way, except at Worlingham where it had been cut to permit the passage of a boat from one bank to the other and at the top of Oulton Broad where they also had to walk round a bad patch.

After lunching at Oulton Broad the party decided to return by the same route. Only two stops were made on the way back. The party of five had set off from Beccles after the harbourmaster, Mr W. Thurgar and Mr H. Gilding of Beccles had advised against it. These gentlemen had taken part in a similar expedition in 1894.

There are many people, in their 50s today, who remember how they played in the snow of 1947 and had "a wonderful time". Miss Jean Overson, pictured here as an eight-year-old at Brandison, Norfolk was one of them. "The grown-ups", she writes "were not so enthusiastic. We were cut off for weeks, too, not days." Photograph shows Roy and Harry Bray trying to cut a way through the snow to the local shop.

"EASTERN DAILY PRESS." March 19. 1947.

Eastern Daily Press

4 a.m. Edition

No. 23,748   NORWICH, WEDNESDAY, MARCH 19, 1947   PRICE 1½d.

THIRTY COUNTIES WITH FLOODS

Fighting To Close The Gap

SECRET

"Critical" in Fenland

THAMES AT PEAK

At least thirty English counties had floods in some parts of them last night, and with rivers still rising and the prospect of more rain the threat of inundation spread even further.

The general outlook in Fenland was "still critical," according to a statement by the Great Ouse Catchment Board yesterday, but the breach in the bank of the Little Ouse had been closed last night after 1000 men had been working all day.

The Board announced that efforts were being made to localise the flooding caused by the breach in the river bank near Ely though water was pouring into the Fens at Cottenham and Willingham. The flooding might extend to a number of Fens but it was hoped that the breach could be sealed.

Severn Position

The outlook at Worcester last night was "very grave," according to Severn Catchment Board officials. The river, still rising, was 15 feet 6 inches above summer level and only 9 inches short of the 1886 flood depth. The city electricity works was surrounded and steel doors were fixed to keep the water out. Drinking water supplies were running low as filtering was affected.

Yesterday was expected to be the peak day in the Thames Valley, where the water was still rising.

All rivers in Lincolnshire, Nottinghamshire, Leicestershire and Rutland were in danger of overflowing. Many roads in Central and South

A Thousand Men Close Gap in Little Ouse Bank

New Flood Threat to Ely: Position Said to be Critical

The 18-yard gap which appeared in the bank of the Little Ouse near Hockwold early yesterday morning and which had flooded over 6000 acres of West Norfolk fenland was closed last night. A thousand men had worked all day passing sandbags a mile along the river bank in an effort to close the gap.

A breach in the banks of the Great Ouse at Over has threatened to isolate Ely. The Ouse Catchment Board stated yesterday that there was a possibility of the flooding extending to a number of fens and the general outlook was still critical.

The position in the Denver Sluice areas has deteriorated. One farm is completely submerged and many acres are waterlogged. Pumps have been standing idle owing to the basins being too full. Because the water in the tidal river has never fallen low enough, sluice gates have remained closed.

Our picture, taken by a staff photographer, shows the desperate efforts being made yesterday to close the gap in the North Bank of the Little Ouse. near Hockwold. After working all day, a thousand men had closed the gap with sandbags last night.

ATOM BOMBS AND NAVY

Admiralty Plans for Research

WORKING PARTY IN WHITEHALL

"We must spend money on research, especially into the effects of the atom bomb on naval warfare," said Mr. John Dugdale, Financial Secretary to the Admiralty, in the House of Commons last night when he introduced the Navy Esti-

evacuated from their houses is Mr. H. Neal, the engineer in charge of the pumping station at Great Fen, Lakenheath, which is under water and

"BRITISH NEVER DAUNTED BY DIFFICULTY"

Premier's Call to Victory Over Economic Troubles

A broadcast message to the nation in which he emphasised the necessity of work if we were to survive was given by Mr. Attlee when he opened a series of party political broadcasts last night.

He said the difficulties which faced the nation were too serious and the challenge too immediate to allow him to indulge in party scores.

Giving the Government's plan for Britain to overcome the difficulties facing her, he reaffirmed his faith in the ability of the British people. "The British people are never daunted by difficulties. The greater the emergency the more readily they respond to the call for service. We shall win in peace just as we did in war," he said. Some people abroad were suggesting that the day of Britain was over. Some of them thought so in the war but they discovered their mistake. "Britain showed the world that she could stand up to terrible odds in defence of the British way of life."

STABILISATION OF LAND PLANS

Mr. Strachey Opens

The Eastern Daily Press of 19th March, 1947 which described the events at Hockwold.

Two men in a rowing boat take supplies to a flooded hamlet, near Newmarket

Upside-down world of Fenland

THE 1947 floods were a disaster for the Fens. More than 40,000 acres of rich agricultural land were inundated. The Great Ouse burst its banks and so did the Little Ouse, the Cam, the Nar, the Wissey and the Lark. Hundreds were evacuated from farms, cottages and villages. Railway lines and roads were swamped, bridges swept away and every kind of farm enterprise ruined. The discharge of flood water was twice as great as anything previously known and people living in Fenland demanded immediate action to prevent a recurrence of the '47 floods.

It may have been the worst but it was certainly not unexpected. Over the centuries, inhabitants of the great Fenland plain, in its massive arc around The Wash, have been aware of the precarious balance between fertility and flooding. Generation after generation has seen its livelihood engulfed by wild waters. Not surprising, for parts of Fenland are as much as four feet below mean sea level and high flood level is up to 12 feet above it. Additionally, the Fen people in recent years have lived in an upside-down world with rivers higher than the surrounding land.

At the end of the 16th century, many areas of The Fens were dry enough for summer pasture but submerged in winter and others squelched all year round. Here the scanty local population developed a special way of life. They called themselves the "Breedlings" and were people apart among whom other Englishmen rarely ventured.

The floors of their flimsy wattle and daub huts, thatched with sedge were often awash. They slept on beds of reeds. For warmth they burned smokey squares of dried peat. They shook with ague, a mosquito-borne endemic malaria and their remedies were brandy and opium.

The Breedlings were protective of their way of life and reacted violently when the first plans for draining the entire fen area were announced in the 17th century. They fought hard and for many decades, sluice gates and other mechanisms installed for drainage purposes required armed guards for protection.

Despite the resistance from the Breedlings a vast network of cuts, drains, sluices and flood storage reservoirs were introduced. Dutch engineers were employed to demonstrate their skill in keeping out the sea. New rivers were created and, in 1651, the first Denver Sluice was constructed across the Ely-Ouse at the lower end of the Hundredfoot River. Then disaster struck again.

In 1713, a combination of high tides and exceptional floods burst the Denver Sluice. The tides flowed unchecked, land was inundated, much of it became derelict and incursions of the sea were frequent; in fact, in 1715, a sturgeon measuring 7 ft 8 in long was captured in Thetford Mill Pond. The Denver Sluice was rebuilt in 1750 by a Swiss engineer. It lasted until 1834 when Sir John Rennie introduced the three main sluice-gates which exist today.

Problems, however, continued. There were major floods in 1905, 1938 and 1939. To counteract continuous sinking, the floodbanks had to be continually raised to give an adequate degree of freeboard and thousands of pounds were spent — with little success.

The Great Floods of 1947 led to a Great Ouse Flood Protection scheme. The problem was not fen drainage, it was the protection of the land from flooding by the failure or overtopping of the river embankments. Engineer, Sir Murdoch MacDonald was appointed to draw up proposals based on a flood about five per cent greater than that of 1947 and coinciding with a period of Spring tides. The Protection Bill was passed by Parliament in 1949 and work began immediately. It was completed in 1964.

Too much water — then suddenly too little

FOLLOWING the blizzard of January, the floods and gales of February and March, Norfolk and Suffolk desperately needed a fine summer to redress the balance and lift people's spirits. Prayers were answered. The summer and autumn of 1947 was one of the sunniest of the century, especially August which was the warmest on record over England as a whole. Even in the far north at Cape Wrath in Scotland, the temperature rose to 80F (27C). September in East Anglia was also dry and warm and so was October.

The Mediterranean summer of 1947 was followed, two years later, by another glorious year. It began with a sunny Easter and continued. From mid-June to September, the temperature was regularly in the 70's and 80's F. Even at Gorleston on the coast there were 54 days above 70F (compare this with 55 days in 1947 and 94 days in 1976).

The Indian summer came to a sticky climax on 5th September when Norwich recorded 91F its hottest September day since 1911. On this day 90F was registered at Belstead, near Ipswich and at Portman Park, Ipswich drew 2-2 with Port Vale in a Division Three South match on one of the warmest evenings that football has ever been played.

During the summer an official drought was declared and there were many forest and railway embankment fires, straining the resources of the fire services in Norfolk and Suffolk.

The three men in this rowing boat are delivering bread and hot soup to the occupants of flooded homes at Kings Dam, Gillingham, near Beccles following the disastrous inundation of 1947. Two of the men have been identified as Mr G.W.Swindells, late manager of Beccles Co-op and Mr Clifford Hambling.

The threat to the Fens was severe Water flowed over the high flood bank at Swaffham Prior Fen, near Upware and was later halted by a double layer of sandbags being placed along the top of the bank. There were serious doubts as to whether the bank itself would break and inundate homes such as the one pictured here.

CHAPTER EIGHT: 1950 — 1959

Fog and floods in the fifties

1950: The longest tornado track ever recorded in Britain was observed from Great Missenden, Bucks to Blakeney, Norfolk during late afternoon on 21st May. The worst damage was in Linslade, Bedfordshire where many houses were entirely unroofed.   In September, a purple sky was seen over east Anglia due to a layer of smoke at 40,000 feet which had originated from forest fires in Canada. Even a blue sun and a blue moon were observed in places. During November and early December scours of "unprecedented severity occurred at Kessingland."

1951: A very wet year. In the Flitcham area, northeast of King's Lynn, 9.43 inches of rain fell during the first three months and the Babingley river flooded roads and fields along its course. More than 200 acres were swamped.

1952: A year which saw a late snowfall accompanied by gale force north-east winds on 29th March and again in November, which was the coldest since 1925. It was a mixed summer, but Gorleston did reach 84F (29C) in late June.

1953: An infamous year due to the catastrophic storm surge along the east coast on the night of 31st January-1st February.   There was widespread flooding and fatalities. The storm was followed by a 36 day absolute drought at Gorleston from 20th February to the end of March. A severe frost on 11th May sent the mercury down to 21F (-6C) at West Raynham. It was still cold on Coronation Day, 2nd June, with temperatures not much above 50F (10C). August was warm — 91F (33C) at Mildenhall on the Glorious Twelfth.   At Thetford on 4th December, there was a reading of 63F (17C).

1954: The winter was variable with 58F (14C) in many places mid January, followed by heavy snow during the latter half of that month. It was also a poor summer. The best days were found along the coast in October with 73F (23C) at Lowestoft on the 17th.

1955: Heavy winter snowfalls especially on 19th February when 19 inches depth was measured in Wellingham. Along the north Norfolk coast, drifts, whipped up by northerly gales, reached 10 feet in height. July was warm with the very rare phenomenon of a rainless month in Bury St Edmunds.

1956: A severe cold spell began around 1st February. At Ipswich and Felixstowe, the temperature failed to rise above 21F (-6C) and snow lay there for 22 days. At Marham, the mercury fell to 2F (-16C) on the 4th. Only one February had been colder this century — that of 1947. Severe fog hit both counties on 18th December. At Lowestoft a ship, *The Ocean Trust* was launched and then completely disappeared from view. The *Eastern Evening News* wrote: "Fog was so dense in the arm of Lake Lothing in which Richards-built ships take the water that the *Ocean Trust* slid gracefully down the ways and then completely diappeared from view."

1957: March was the mildest this century. The aurora borealis was seen at Marham on the night of 27th/28th.   A heatwave brought temperatures soaring to 93F (33C) at Mildenhall on 29th June and monthly sunshine records were broken.   Violent thunderstorms were set off by the heat early in July. A schoolboy was killed and two others knocked unconscious when lightning struck a bell tent at Mundesley on the 5th.   At Outwell, the lightning temporarily blinded the driver of a van which left the road and plunged into the water of Well Creek. Two died.   Another severe storm, this time with wind gusts up to 104 mph, was recorded on 1st November. Roads at New Costessey, North Walsham, Fakenham, Sculthorpe and Burnham Market were blocked by fallen trees and a family had a lucky escape when a chimney stack crashed through the roof of a house in Mill Road, Wells.

1958: Between January and April there were 38 days when snow fell at Sprowston. It was also very wet.. In their issue of 4th July, the *Bury Free Press* wrote: "Rain, rain and still more rain, day after day, night after night. And still no end of it in sight. The month just ended will go down as one of the wettest ever known. The June rainfall was 4.09 inches, the highest on record for that month since records began at Mildenhall Station in 1936."

1959: An outstanding summer. In June, Gorleston averaged over 10 hours a day and the temperatures exceeded 93F (33.9C) at Cromer on 5th July. September was rainless at Terrington St Clement and East Bergholt and, even as late as 3rd October, Mildenhall was recording 82F (28C).

Christine Williams, now of Little Melton, Norwich remembers the thunderstorms of July 1957. She writes: "I was in Garden Street, Cromer with my sister and aunt when a heavy storm broke and we had to shelter in a shop doorway. All of a sudden there was a bright flash of light followed by a crash of thunder and what I now believe to be a ball of lightning rolled down the street, past us, and collided with the side of a building across the street. As you can imagine we were very frightened and I remember running as fast as I could in the opposite direction and taking a taxi home. I was aged about seven at the time."

This scene near Wroxham, Norfolk shows a motorist clearing snow off the arm of the signpost after the short sharp snowstorm of 14th December, 1952, which followed the Great Smog.

Smog — the greatest killer of all

5th — 8th December, 1952

SO dense was the fog which descended on East Anglia during the evening of Friday 5th December, 1952 that traffic moved at walking pace and, in Ipswich, AA men were summoned to lead vehicles to higher ground.

This was a water fog, a genuine "peasouper" which lasted four days and nights and, in London, was one of the greatest mass killers of the 20th century. Nobody knows how many died as a direct result of the London fog but the death rate rose by more than 4,000 and many of these were people who were living near the industrial banks of the Thames.

In the bigger cities, including Ipswich and Norwich, visibility at times was down to 10-15 yards and in many other areas it was nil. Trains from London, including the "East Anglian express" were more than two hours late, and some didn't arrive at all. Two passengers on the 2.55 pm Yarmouth to Liverpool Street were injured on Friday when the train collided with another passenger train in Ipswich station.

On the nights of Saturday, Sunday and Monday it was impossible for pedestrians to move about freely in familiar surroundings. Newspapers described it as the "Great Smog" — the type known to those of the last century as a filthy, black Victorian "peasouper" and thought to be virtually extinct.

The fog contained localised pockets of a highly poisonous nature due to the concentration of sulphur dioxide and associated gasses emanating from factory chimneys. It was particularly bad along the industrial waterfronts where people suffered violent fits of coughing and animals, particularly cattle, were asphixiated.

Another cliff fall at Sidestrand leaves this house precariously placed on the edge of a precipice. Over the years hundreds of fishermen's cottages, terraced houses and clifftop cottages have slipped into the sea in Norfolk and Suffolk. At Lowestoft, a public inquiry was held in December 1950 into a proposal to spend £83,000 on a coast protection scheme to arrest erosion at Kessingland. The inquiry was told that only constant maintenance of the sea wall stood between Suffolk and disaster by erosion or flood. The proposal was given the go ahead and work began in September 1952 (see right). Four months later came the greatest tidal surge of all.

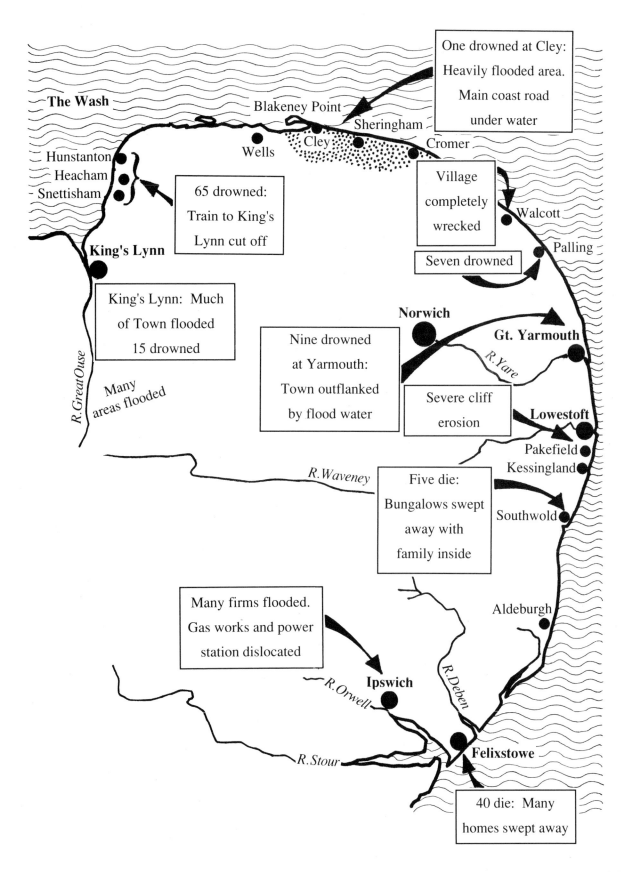

The Wash

Blakeney Point

Sheringham

One drowned at Cley:
Heavily flooded area.
Main coast road
under water

Cley

Wells

Cromer

Hunstanton
Heacham
Snettisham

65 drowned:
Train to King's
Lynn cut off

King's Lynn

Village
completely
wrecked

Walcott

Seven drowned

Palling

King's Lynn: Much
of Town flooded
15 drowned

Norwich

Gt. Yarmouth

R. Yare

R. Great Ouse

Nine drowned
at Yarmouth:
Town outflanked
by flood water

Many
areas flooded

Severe cliff
erosion

Lowestoft

Pakefield
Kessingland

R. Waveney

Five die:
Bungalows swept
away with
family inside

Southwold

Aldeburgh

Many firms flooded.
Gas works and power
station dislocated

R. Deben

R. Orwell

Ipswich

R. Stour

Felixstowe

40 die: Many
homes swept away

Greatest peacetime disaster that Britain has ever known

31st January — 1st February, 1953

THE night of Saturday 31st January, 1953 brought to Britain one of the greatest peacetime disasters in her history. A storm surge, driven by hurricane-force, north-westerly winds whipped up the waters of the North Sea into massive tidal levels which then smashed through sea wall fortifications, breaching more than 1,400 sites from Lincolnshire to Kent. When the water subsided, 307 people had been drowned, along with thousands of cattle, pigs, sheep and poultry. More than 32,000 people had been evacuated from their homes and 1,000 miles of coastline flooded.

For East Anglia it was the most catastrophic tragedy in modern history and one that lives vividly in the memory of people who experienced the nightmare of the sea suddenly engulfing their houses. There were almost 100 deaths in the two counties and thousands of people were driven from their homes, many not to see them again for many months.

It began when a deep depression of enormous intensity moved from Iceland in a south-easterly direction on Friday 30th January. Gale force winds struck the north coast of Scotland late that night. Next morning the average wind speed in the Orkneys was 90 mph with gusts up to 125 mph. The gale forced a tremendous volume of Atlantic water, estimated at more than four billion cubic yards, into the North Sea. In addition there was a spring tide which raised the sea 10 feet above normal. The agents were displaying all the classic symptoms associated with a North Sea surge.

A furious wind blew across the British Isles. In the Irish Sea it was hurricane-force and the British Railways Ferry, *MV Victoria*, crossing from Stranraer to Larne in the early hours of Saturday morning, had run into the teeth of the gale and was listing badly. The captain sent an SOS and then gave orders to abandon the ship. Men formed a human chain to get women and children out of the lounge and into the lifeboats. With the wireless operator still transmitting, the ship keeled over and sank, having drifted across the Irish Sea to a point close to the comparative calm of Belfast Lough. The death toll was 132 and included women and children who had been thrown into the sea when their lifeboat overturned.

Early on Saturday evening, BBC news bulletins gave details of the terrible shipping accident and described how lifeboats had picked up 44 survivors. It was the greatest disaster suffered by any British Merchant vessel in peacetime for 25 years.

The coastal people of East Anglia would have heard on the wireless of the tragedy in the Irish Sea but the significance of what had happened in relation to their perilous position was not yet apparent. They were certainly aware of heavy winds and high tides but on this late January day it was not unusual and there was little anxiety.

Many had spent the Saturday afternoon going about their usual tasks. Many had played in, or attended the local football match, including King's Lynn ambulance driver Bertie Hart, who had noticed that outgoing tides were not getting away from the Great Ouse as they should have done. There was still a lot of water in the river when the incoming tides came. In Sea Palling, many villagers were getting ready for their regular Saturday whist drive while sailing enthusiasts right round the coast were carrying out renovations to their boats and, in some cases, securing them in readiness for what could be a wild night. The staff of the Suffolk Hotel in Lowestoft were preparing to greet members of the town Choral Society for their annual dinner. Others stayed indoors, pulling themselves closer to the fire and listening to "Saturday Night Theatre" on the wireless.

All day the wind was blowing but not with the severity attained in Scotland, where gusts were still in excess of 100 mph. The first indication that all was not well was at Aberdeen where the sea rose 2.5 feet above the predicted level. The great tide then rolled south into the ever-increasing bottleneck of the North Sea. As it did so, the water rose higher and higher.

At 5.30 pm water began to pour into the town centre of Sutton-on-Sea, Lincolnshire and, at Mablethorpe, the concrete sea walls were smashed into pieces. It was only a matter of minutes before the town centre was flooded. As cars, furniture and household belongings were washed away the great evacuation began, 6,000 being taken away from the coastal strip that divides the two towns. At one time the sea penetrated several miles inland behind Sutton and sand was deposited up to depths of eight feet all over the town. As the tragedies began to unfold — 16 drowned at Sutton and another 20 in the area near Skegness — the tide rolled south towards the eastern coast of The Wash.

The warning now went down the line. To the county police stations and on to the sub divisions. Police with the most vulnerable waterfronts to supervise were advised to pass the warning to the

One of the seaside bungalows at Hunstanton along the Wash coastline which took the full force of the surge. People were rescued from the roofs of buildings and one family was found in the cab of a dragline where they had shut themselves for safety.

owners of premises that were likely to flood. By 7 pm, harbour masters, sluice keepers, river board officials and county council officials were monitoring the progress of the tide which was now thrusting against sea walls, softening up mile upon mile of defences and undermining the subsoil.

The eastern shores of The Wash were the first in Norfolk to go under, simultaneously overwhelmed at about 7.35 pm. The crest of the shingle ridge between Wolferton and Hunstanton was cut down and carried inland. There were 40 breaches in the Snettisham Bank. The strength of the waves smashed the sea wall at Heacham South Beach and demolished the parapet of the Heacham North Beach wall over a length of 300 yards.

It was the stretch of coast between Hunstanton and King's Lynn that took the brunt of the early assault upon Norfolk. At South Beach, where 40 holiday bungalows had been built, a wall of water surged over the natural bank and swept away the homes. The occupants, including many American servicemen and their families, stood no chance.

Among them was Derek Stubbins, a 14-year-old schoolboy who had been elected house captain the day before. He arrived home just before the barriers were breached and was drowned with the rest of his family. His friend Janet Papworth was luckier. She had been invited to a friend's birthday party in Hunstanton and said goodbye to her mother and three sisters during the afternoon. She never saw

Women and children fleeing from their homes on the beach at Snettisham took refuge in the cab of a gravel pit dredger. They spent the night watching, and listening, to the violent sea, wondering if they would survive. They did. Picture shows the rescuers with stretcher hurrying to the scene. Some of the bungalows at Snettisham were moved eight or nine hundred yards.

*from their original site and remained more or less whole.
Others were smashed into matchwood and only about six were
left habitable between the village and the sea.*

them again.

The American forces, stationed at Sculthorpe, were among the first to arrive at South Beach with rescue equipment. One of them, USAF Corporal Reis Leming, a non-swimmer, attempted to get to the disaster scene in a rubber dinghy. "Boy, it took some keeping into the wind and sometimes was right under the water," he told the *Eastern Daily Press*, "but I managed to get near the ruins of the bungalows and get people into the dinghy. Shucks, it wasn't much."

But it was. Leming travelled the whole length of the Hunstanton bungalows, returning time and time again to take people off the roofs. A gale was blowing, there was a terrific current and he was in great danger from floating debris. Single handedly, this 22-year-old rescued 27 people and he was in the water from 8.45 pm until 4.45 am when he collapsed from exposure and slipped into unconsciousness. For his actions that night, Reis Leming was awarded the George Medal.

Sixteen Americans were among the 32 who died at Hunstanton and it would have been more if it were not for Leming and his colleagues who arrived within an hour of the first breach. The coroner at the Hunstanton inquest said: "Our American friends will leave behind an enduring memory of courage and assistance in these troubled times."

There was more tragedy at nearby Snettisham. The Beckerton family who lived in a bungalow near the beach had just bought their first television set and were settling down for an evening's viewing with their three children. With them were two foster children who lived with Alfred Walton and his wife a few hundred yards away. As the evening wore on and the weather worsened, Frederick Beckerton and his son Peter decided to see if everything was OK with the Waltons.

When they got outside the sea was coming over the bank and it was clear that neither family would survive in their wooden bungalows. While Peter struggled through waist-high water in a bid to rescue the Waltons, Frederick returned to find the sea in his house. He snatched sheets from the linen cupboard, lashed his small boat to the verandah, helped the children into the boat one by one and gave them orders to bail out the water with cake tins as the waves crashed over them. The couple then stood chest high in the surging sea, hanging on to the boat. They saw their home collapse. Timber and furniture crashed into them as it swept past on the surge. A complete bungalow sailed past. They wondered if Peter had made it to the Waltons.

No-one will ever know. He was last seen struggling through the icy black waters with

Assessing the damage at Snettisham where 25 people were drowned in a holiday camp about half a mile from the beach front. When the floods receded scores of National Service "erks" from RAF West Raynham, spent days filling sandbags to repair breaches in the shingle bank.

the gale at its worst. The Waltons were among 25 people to die at Snettisham and Peter Beckerton's body was washed ashore five weeks later. For his sacrificial act of bravery he was to be posthumously awarded the Albert Medal.

His family survived that terrible night but it meant hanging on for seven hours until they were rescued by the village policeman, Pc Henry Nobbs who, with the aid of a rope, led them to dry land.

Not far away the crew and passengers on the 7.27 pm Hunstanton to King's Lynn train were having their own share of the drama. The train not only collided with a wall of water near the station but one of the floating bungalows struck the engine and put it out of action. With the sea closing in the crew

effected repairs and, using the floorboards of the tender as fuel managed to crawl back to Hunstanton.

Further south, the stretch of coastline immediately to the west and east of the Great Ouse successfully withstood the onslaught but the tidal embankments of the river itself were overtopped for 14 miles down to the Denver Sluice and there were eight breaches in the bank. So sudden was the rise of water in King's Lynn that one-fifth of the town was inundated up to a depth of six feet and hundreds of people were trapped in upstairs rooms. Police toured the town with loud hailers urging people to evacuate their houses. A rumour was circulated to the effect that the Denver Sluice had blown up, the tidal banks were crumbling and Lynn would soon be totally inundated.

Almost 2,000 people were evacuated from King's Lynn that night but 15 drowned. Some were lucky, including 15-year-old John Ebbs and his mate Harold Scott who balanced on top of a letter box outside South Lynn post office as the sea swirled around them. Eventually they managed to swim to the Jolly Farmers pub.

Meanwhile the storm was attacking the North Norfolk coastline and surging across farmland. Farmer, Peter Hancock opened the front door of his house at Burnham Overy and found the sea lapping at the step. It had advanced inland by a mile. Regulars enjoying a Saturday night drink at The Victoria in Holkham also found the sea outside and helped to ferry refugees to safety along the inside bank of Holkham Park. The shingle bank at Blakeney collapsed and a tidal wave smashed into the town centre. It took everything in its wake and carcasses of dead animals were seen floating with furniture and dead fish. A 30-yard stretch of Sheringham promenade was swept away. So powerful was the force of the sea that foam soared high above the clifftop hotels, cascading down chimneys and tearing tiles off roofs. Wells lifeboat was lifted from its moorings and washed up on the outskirts of Blakeney, 10 miles from its base. One motorist on the Holkham Road met a wall of water coming towards him. Thinking it was a temporary, and not unusual winter flood, he drove on and found his car floating. That was the signal for action. He scrambled out and looked for the wall which encircles Holkham Park. Sitting astride it he heaved himself along with the sea smashing against him. Eventually he found a stranded bus and gratefully joined passengers on the upper deck.

All along the north Norfolk coast people took their most precious possessions upstairs and hoped their house wouldn't collapse. There was a bizarre incident at Marsh Farm, Burnham Norton where a farmer with a sow and a new litter stopped a floating sofa, carefully placed the animals on it and retired with his family to the upstairs room.

continued on page 87

Day Hut to Let, says the sign but this is all that is left of the little wooden bungalows that succumbed to the sea at Heacham. Nine people died when the sea wall was breached at about 6.45 pm on the Saturday evening — about an hour after the tide broke through at Sutton in Lincolnshire. The timing is interesting for it was after midnight when the surge reached Canvey Island in Essex where 58 people perished. Could they have been saved?

*People in King's Lynn stare, almost disbelievingly, as the flood waters rise in London Road.
Many escaped along the London Road, clinging on to the railings but in Ouse Avenue and the
maze of streets running nearby, the water rose to a depth of six feet.*

There's none of the usual childish gaiety on the faces of these youngsters — the floods hit too quickly for their resilience to operate. They were waiting, some with their parents, in a King's Lynn reception centre where they were taken after the sea surged down the Great Ouse and flooded their homes. So heavy was the spilling over the banks of the Ouse and the River Nar that many people were trapped in their houses, unable to escape. At West Lynn a series of breaches in the river bank flooded factories to a depth of several feet. Land at West Lynn lay under five feet of water for more than two weeks.

*Top picture: The great evacuation is underway in the Wisbech Road area of King's Lynn.
Above: An American abandoned his car near Wiveton when the Glaven burst its banks. Five
escaped, just in time.*

The sandbags were full — then came the task of filling the breach in the Beach Road embankment at Wells.

When the waters receded, sow and litter were found safe and well, still on the sofa! The town of Wells-next-the-Sea sustained heavy damage. Houses in the north-west part of the town were swamped and the station was under water. A 160-ton vessel was picked up by the waves and deposited on the quay where it remained for several months.

A 2,000 million gallon torrent swept aside the shingle bank protecting the partially reclaimed Cley and Salthouse marshes, tore at the cliffs behind the coast road and devastated the villages. One person was drowned at Cley. Gordon Lee, aged 19, was one of the many who escaped as the sea poured into the village street. "I went to release my parents' pigs from their sties", he said, "when suddenly I heard a tremendous roar. All I could see when I turned round was water. It seemed to reach from the ground to the sky."

So profound are the memories of that night that Mr Lee has published a book about the ordeal faced by the residents of Salthouse, Blakeney and Cley under his nickname Buttercup Joe. He explains how he was marooned on top of his shed in darkness and repeated attempts to reach him by boat failed because of the strength of the tide. He managed to climb a tree

to gain more height where he found some companions — hundreds of screaming rats.

Deep floods penetrated the Wiveton and Glaven Valleys. A 73-year-old woman was drowned in Wiveton when a crushing brutal wave poured into her kitchen. The picturesque village was almost obliterated; at least 30 houses were destroyed and another 20 so severely damaged as to be uninhabitable. The uncompleted sea wall at Walcott was outflanked and destroyed and an empty 4,000-ton coaster deposited on the beach. Here, the 15 foot protective cliffs were reduced to just four feet high in places when the water receded.

The towering tidal waters crashed against the defences at Cromer and caused enormous damage to the pier and the pavilion. The door of the lifeboat station was ripped apart and Henry Blogg's much-loved lifeboat carried away and dumped on its port side against the east sea-front wall. As the waves tugged at seaside chalets and cast them out to sea, local crabmen hauled their boats to the top of the steep, cobbled causeway known as the Gangway — and then watched in alarm as the waves came to within feet of where they stood.

Overstrand and Mundesley, two villages which

Continued on page 91

Salthouse is some way from the sea, but on Saturday 31st January, 1953 it became a waterside village that looked desolate and abandoned. The floods breached the sea wall, surged across the marshes and, in 30 minutes, the village was overwhelmed. Amazingly, only one person died — an elderly lady who was swept through her kitchen window. This picture was taken as the waters receded.

This picture, perhaps more than any others, sums up the devastation and heartbreak that faced the victims of the 1953 floods. This was Salthouse, an inland village, where residents returned to search for their belongings. There had been no warning. As Michael Pollard explained in his book Tidal Surge: "When the sea bursts into your home in the middle of the night, you do not wait to assemble a change of underwear, your toothbrush and flannel, your insurance policy and bank book. Sheer pressure of time forced rescuers to place an embargo on everything but human cargo." Hilda Grieve in her study of the disaster wrote: "The sea's achievement in one night challenges comparison with that of the Luftwaffe in six years."

The River Glaven at Cley, once a small river which flowed from Glandford and Wiveton in north Norfolk, was transformed into a wild, destructive fast-flowing torrent as the sea burst through, completely submerging the coast road.

Ipswich did not escape. As the Orwell burst its banks, flood water swirled menacingly in many areas of the city.

had suffered so badly through erosion in far less violent storms, were battered. The mass concrete wall was overturned at Overstrand and the promenade smashed to fragments at Mundesley. At Sea Palling it was even worse. The waves burst through a gap in the dunes, engulfed all the buildings at the seaward end of the village and swept thousands of tons of sand up the village street where it lay in drifts up to five feet deep. The people stood no chance and many were swept away to their deaths before they had even realised what was happening.

Seven drowned in Sea Palling. They included the landlord of the Lifeboat Inn who was taken by the sea as he tried to reach a rescue boat and a woman who had actually managed to escape to a high bank with her sister and, at the moment of safety, slipped into the water. Two more elderly ladies climbed on to the roof of their bungalow but, with the gale at its zenith and the freezing spray constantly attacking them, one died of exposure. Two children of the same family drowned — an elder daughter who was returning home after delivering the evening's papers and her little sister who slipped off her father's back as he struggled through the water.

In his book *North Sea Surge*, Michael Pollard tells the story of Florence Ridley who was preparing supper for her elderly parents at Sea Palling when a friend called to say that the sea had come over. They went outside and heard cries of help from across the road. "We got to the garden gate", said Florence, "when a huge wave bowled us back into the bungalow. I managed to get mum inside. We could see the sea sweeping across our garden. We saw the hedge go under and then the fence. All was one sheet of water, hissing and roaring its way over the fields."

Florence, with her mother and father, a friend who was staying with them and a mother and daughter from next door, found a ladder and climbed onto the roof. Huddled together by the chimney stack, they waited to be rescued. "The wind was tearing past at a great rate and the sea was rising rapidly. The roof was wet and slippery. We saw animals and trees and large objects float by but we clung on for what seemed a lifetime." They spent five and a half hours on the roof, but survived.

On either side of Sea Palling, at Eccles and Horsey, waves overtopped the concrete sea walls and cut away the dunes behind. At Eccles the wall collapsed over a length of 1.5 miles.

Further down the coast many people of Great Yarmouth were enjoying a normal Saturday night out. The pubs were fairly full, the cinema was packed and there was dancing in the clubs. The first signs of trouble came when people crossing the Haven Bridge watched in horror as a wall of water roared up from the harbour mouth. The word went around Yarmouth like wildfire. Warnings were flashed on the cinema screen, boys raced round the town knocking on doors, the police shouted to pub customers.... "The sea is breaking through. Run." Simultaneously, the Breydon Wall, well known to Broads holidaymakers, collapsed and millions of gallons of sea water came surging across the marshes through gaps in the railway embankment, drowning grazing cattle and ponies and pouring into the town centre. It rushed into the Cobholm and Southtown areas and was joined by the overflowing water from the River Yare. The town which had been attacked by the sea in front was now outflanked by the Breydon Waters from the rear. Great Yarmouth was isolated and all main lines of communication were severed. Within minutes, nine people were dead, more than 1,000 homes flooded and the greatest rescue operation in the town's history was under way.

Trevor Westgate, the youngest reporter on the *Great Yarmouth Mercury* remembers the brutal force of the wind as he and his family joined the thousands of evacuees from the flooded areas of Cobholm and Southtown. "One ferocious gust took me off my feet and blew me across the pavement as I passed the Town Hall," he said. "We joined the others on the bridge to look down on the water hissing and foaming beneath us on its way to fill the basin of Breydon Water. The perception of real danger grew as it became apparent that there would be no stopping this night's tide with the puny walls which lined the

A whist drive was in progress in the Nissen Hut that the people of Sea Palling used as a village hall, when the vicar came in and announced that the sea was coming through. The whist drive came to an abrupt halt, people rushed outside, and seeing for themselves the unbridled power of the North Sea, immediately organised the rescue operations. Seven people were drowned in Sea Palling that night but it could have been more.

River Yare."

A family in Queens Road spent a night on the roof of their bungalow before being rescued. In Ferry Lane, bordering the Yare, people attempted to barricade their homes but the raging flood of water tore these down and, as the electricity failed, the streets were plunged into darkness. Dead animals floated swiftly past with rabbit hutches, still containing the animals. The water rushed into Southtown railway station, where a signalman was marooned in his box for more than 21 hours.

A scene of unbelievable desolation was revealed at dawn. Six people, mostly elderly women living alone, had drowned and another three died of shock. One was found entangled in an iron bedstead, completely submerged. The corpses of cattle floated on the marshes. The sea front, still completely engulfed by the watery avalanche, presented a picture of utter despair.

In Suffolk, across the estuary of the Yare, there was more desolation, more tragedy, more courage as sea walls burst and the sand hills were inundated. In some places the floods ran three or four miles inland and reached a depth of 10 feet. Lowestoft, however, escaped relatively lightly. Here the new sea wall, which had cost the Corporation a controversial £300,000 just after the war, saved the town from the kind of major disaster that had struck Yarmouth.

There was no loss of life, no serious injury but even so the sea swept through the old Beach Village, swamped the Ness Point gas works, cutting off supplies to the whole town and some 400 houses flooded.

Among those who had an unpleasant experience were 40 children, trapped in St John's Church, as the waters rose. The children, who had been at a social with their helpers, retreated to a point above the altar steps and began yelling for help. Two policemen waded chest deep to reach the church and one dived under the muddy water to turn the door handle. The water in the church was too deep so the policemen waited for more help. A local boatman turned up and tried to row up the aisle but the pews were now floating in the water and caused too much obstruction. The policemen had to act quickly so they carried the children one by one from the altar steps to the boat until it was full. The boatman rowed off with his passengers and returned three more times to repeat the manoeuvre.

Terrific winds which battered Southwold during the day died down in the early evening, but as night fell the sea began its awesome advance on the town, and then struck like a battering ram from both north and south. Two sisters, aged 80 and 76, a 39-year-old mother and her four year old son drowned. The body of a fifth woman was never found. All the fatalities occurred in the Ferry Road where some 10 bungalows were completely ruined and another 20 badly damaged. Ferry Road

The fight to fill the gaps in the defences at Sea Palling before the next high tides were due, slipped into top gear in the first week of February. Sandbags were filled on the spot by troops. There was no shortage of labour for the task — civilians were recruited from all over Britain to join National Servicemen.

Another incredible scene from Sea Palling where sand and shingle almost buried a car.

almost disappeared after the water receded, leaving a mass of shingle eight to ten feet deep.

One American family was saved after their bungalow on Ferry Road had been carried 400 yards by the sea and dumped on the marshes. Mr and Mrs Sorick and their baby, who were entertaining four friends at the time, climbed onto the roof and clung on until they were rescued by two seamen in a rowing boat.

From below South Green, Southwold to the Pleasure Pier end not a single bungalow survived. These 30 summer dwellings were just swept out to sea. A huge sheet of water spread from the bottom of Constitution Hill from California across the marshes to Blackshore and beyond. At the north end of the town flooding stretched from the boating lake over the fields in Reydon and down to Mights Bridge. The town was totally cut off for 48 hours.

At dusk on Saturday evening the Aldeburgh fishermen had returned from a stormy day at sea with some good catches. They knew it was going to be a high tide so they tied their boats well up the shore as safe as possible from the marauding waves. Several hours later much of Aldeburgh was under water and the boats were being used to evacuate more than 100 people from their homes.

The sea had broken through at Crag Path, crashed over the wall near the Brudenell Hotel and run through Hertford Place into the High Street. Yachts, still tied to their moorings, had been carried down the River Alde and across flooded marshes. The road to Slaughden was impassable and the boatmen there had lost every piece of gear. Hundreds of tons of shingle were piled up high against the houses in Crag Path. The marshes surrounding the town resembled a huge lake. Sheds, dustbins, pigs and

This was Sunday morning, 1st February and the great rescue in Yarmouth continued as ladders were placed under bedroom windows from boats borrowed from The Broads.

chickens were floating about. Many head of livestock were lost.

No-one died in Aldeburgh during the invasion but Danny Mann drowned a few days later as he helped the Army repair the breaches on the sea and river walls.

At the west end of Felixstowe on the Landguard Peninsula, by the estuary of the River Orwell, was a colony of post-war prefabs which faced inland. All their inhabitants found themselves fighting for their lives as a surging icy torrent smashed down the wall lining the estuary and engulfed the houses like a violent nightmare. For the residents of the prefabs at the junction of Langer Road and Orford Road the margin between life and death was a matter of seconds as the sea struck with incredible force.

Some drowned in their beds as the water quickly reached the eaves. Others, many in nightclothes, had to scramble onto the roofs as the only place of safety. There they clung in desperation until the early hours of the morning when the first rescues were made by police using boats from Butlin's fun fair. The magnitude of the disaster unfolded at daylight. Twenty eight people who had clung to roofs had been washed away and drowned. Survivors said that in the darkness all that could be heard was the roaring of the water and the screaming of terrified women. Every prefab was moved from its site, some as much as 200 yards.

In all, 40 people drowned in Felixstowe on that terrible night. One man, Mr William Leggatt who was alone in his house told the *East Anglian Daily Times:* "The house was rocking and creaking on its foundations so I got out and started to swim down Levington Road. The current drove me along and

The force of the sea smashed through bricks and concrete in seconds. As flooding swept to Haddiscoe and Acle marshes, the Haddiscoe Gap was reopened and the railway line left suspended.

when I looked behind, my house was following me down the road. I reached the Station Hotel and found the occupants were asleep. They couldn't believe the tale I told them."

One family went upstairs to escape the sea but very quickly it was a foot deep in their bedroom. They banged a hole in the ceiling and climbed into the loft, praying the water wouldn't rise that far. It didn't. The Hillary family, living in Langer Road watched with horror as the prefabs swept by. "We saw a woman washed off the roof of a house as it floated past", said Mrs Hillary. "One little girl and her father clung on to the roof from half past twelve until seven in the morning."

Hardly one community around the coast of Norfolk and Suffolk escaped the trauma of the disastrous floods of 1953. Ordinary people became heroes overnight, going to the rescue of neighbours and complete strangers. Many died carrying out acts of immense courage and others bear emotional scars that will remain with them for ever.

The sea also devastated Essex. Eight died at Harwich and 3,000 were made homeless. Thirty seven drowned at Jaywick when the sea overwhelmed a housing estate. There were tragedies at Great Wakering, Foulness and Twekes Creek. At Canvey, the whole island was under water, 58 died and everyone was evacuated. Central London caught the tail end of the catastrophe. Water lapped the top of the parapet along the Victoria and Chelsea embankments and defences were overtopped by a few inches at Greenwich, Woolwich and London Bridge. In Kent, the southern shores of the Thames Estuary and towns and villages from Woolwich to the North Foreland were badly flooded.

The disaster quickly became a matter of intense personal anxiety to people all over the world, particularly among those who had friends or relatives living in East Anglia close to the sea. The problems seemed endless, for apart from the toll it had taken in human lives and suffering, there was the heavy damage the storm had inflicted on the defences, on agricultural land and on industry.

After the mopping up, gifts began to pour in for the people of Norfolk and Suffolk. There was furniture, bedding, fuel, clothes, sandbags, money, offers of

There was no loss of life at Lowestoft, but some 400 houses were flooded and gas supplies were completely cut off. This is a view of the Harbour Hotel..

accommodation. The first essentials were to feed and house the homeless and destitute, find foster parents for the orphans and trace those, who in the chaos of the moment, had not been accounted for. Rest centres, feeding centres, mobile canteens and distribution centres were set up. Eventually there was Government help for farmers and urgent high level consultations on the need to reinstate tidal defences.

Those who lived through the disaster of 1953 have never forgotten it — a fact proved by the stories of tragedy, resoucefulness, courage that emerge in

local newspapers throughout the two counties on each anniversary. East Anglia has never forgotten the indomitable spirit of the people of King's Lynn, Hunstanton, Snettisham, Heacham, Holkham, Wells, Cromer, Sea Palling, Yarmouth, Lowestoft, Southwold, Aldeburgh, Orford, Felixstowe and hundreds of other, smaller communities, right along the coastal fringe.

The 1953 tidal surge has earned a place in history as the most catastrophic event ever recorded in Britain — and one that must never be repeated.

The Felixstowe Times

No. 1,820.   SATURDAY, FEBRUARY 7, 1953.   Registered for Transmission as a Newspaper and for Canadian Magazine Post.   Twopence.

FLOOD SPECIAL

THE PEOPLE'S SPIRIT WAS UNBROKEN AMID THE SCENE OF HAVOC

39 DROWNED, MANY INJURED IN TOWN'S NIGHT OF HORROR

Felixstowe this week is a grief-stricken town. Thirty-nine people lost their lives in the disastrous flood which engulfed the West end of the town shortly after midnight on Saturday.

The bodies of 38 of the victims have been recovered; one is still missing.

The ages of the victims ranged from babies of a few months to elderly people of over 80, and in more than one instance complete families perished in the deluge.

Hundreds have been rendered homeless and some have lost all their possessions. They are now accommodated in hotels, boarding-houses or in the homes of friends.

When the inquest on 30 of the victims was opened on Tuesday, the Coroner, Major Norman Butters, described the tragedy as probably the worst in the town's history·

First warning of the impending disaster came shortly after 11.30 p.m. on Saturday with telephone messages to the police station of flooding at Felixstowe Ferry, the R.A.F. Station, Landguard Fort and Landguard Point; then came a report that a woman had been swept away at Landguard Fort, but that her

Here is a scene in the West end of Felixstowe, where the great tide claimed 39 victims. Sunday morning's picture in the Langer Road area as rescues of marooned householders were made by scores of small craft.

MEMORIAL SERVICE — FEB. 15

A UNITED memorial service for those who lost their lives in the flood has been arranged at St. John's Church on Sunday, February 15th, at 3 p.m. The preacher will be the Bishop of St. Edmundsbury and Ipswich, Dr. Richard Brook, and the service will be conducted by the vicar of St. John's, Canon W. Cocks. Lessons will be read by the Rev. D. Allen

Morale of Homeless was "Marvellous"

Interviewed by the "Felixstowe Times," Capt. A. E. Smith, chairman of the Urban District Council, said: "The people of Felixstowe little thought when they responded so generously to the Lynmouth flood disaster that we should so soon be called upon to face one of our own.

"The town has suffered a grievous blow and the greatest sympathy has been felt and shown to the victims of the flood both at the Ferry and the West End.

"It is difficult to find words adequately to express the pride and satisfaction which I feel towards the hundreds of people who have helped and continued to help from the early hours of Sunday. Our thanks to the hotels and private houses that have taken the hundreds of evacuees, whose morale has been simply marvellous. So many of them have lost homes and everything they possess."

He added that his appeal fund would serve as a means whereby those who had escaped could express gratitude by helping others to get back to normal life.

RELIEF FUND | 89 SHEEP

The Felixstowe Times tells the horrific story.

A seaside town under the sea. Prefab residents are rescued from Felixstowe as their nightmare continues into the following day.

An early-morning view of the devastation at Southwold, where a great wall of water struck both the north and south ends of the town.

The young Queen Elizabeth, along with other members of the Royal Family, toured the stricken areas, giving what comfort she could to the brave and beleaguered people of the east coast. Here she is in Felixstowe.

Cambridge undergraduate volunteers helped hundreds of policemen, servicemen and river workers in the day-and-night battle to close the breach in the banks of the Great Ouse, at Magdalen near King's Lynn. When this picture was taken on 5th February, 1953 water from the river still flowed steadily into the surrounding countryside and many thousands of acres of fenland and agricultural land, as well as some villages, were still inundated.

Once more into the breach...

WITH hundreds of gaps in the sea wall all round the coast of Norfolk and Suffolk and a high spring tide predicted for mid-February, a colossal effort was required to seal the breaches — high enough, wide enough and strong enough. It was a desperate race against time.

More than 30,000 men were soon at work. Many came from the armed forces and, in East Anglia, they were mostly Americans. They were joined by students, farmers, farm workers and volunteers from every walk of life. In biting wind, driving rain, great flurries of snow and the date of 14th February as an inexorable deadline, civilians and servicemen worked side by side. They rescued livestock, cleared away the debris and blocked the breached defences with sandbags, stones and any other material that came to hand.

The weather was appalling and huge labour forces were isolated on the sea marshes, without shelter, in conditions of misery. One of the worst breaches was in the banks of the tidal Ouse and here, 130 men from the RAF worked day and night to keep pace with the rising tides and protect well-populated West Lynn from an even greater disaster.

On the section between Happisburgh and Winterton, improvised groynes and brushwood defences were erected to build up the depleted beach. At Sea Palling, 16,650 feet of new sea wall were constructed. A new wall was built at Horsey to replace the one which had been demolished. It was extended southward to a point where the dunes were high and wide. Steel groynes were erected at Overstrand and defences all the way down the Suffolk coast were heightened and reinforced.

Ipswich in February, 1956 when both Suffolk and Norfolk were cut off by drifts. Two years later it was even worse.

Buried in a snowdrift for 40 hours

20th February, 1956: 26th February, 1958

A HIGH pressure system which extended from Russia to Scandinavia kept most of England dry and intensely cold during mid-February, 1956. However, the clouds which gathered over the east coast produced immense quantities of fine powdered snow which were swept into great drifts all the way down the coastal fringe from Yorkshire to Kent. In these conditions, rivers and Broads were frozen, thousands of fish were killed, main roads were impassable and snow ploughs worked throughout the night.

For Norfolk, it was the coldest winter since 1947. On 20th February, drifts brought chaos to the county's road and rail system. Eastern County buses became stuck fast at Trimingham, Holt and Cromer and, at Bacton, a North Walsham jeweller spent 40 hours in his car buried in a snowdrift. He wondered at times if he would ever be found.

Conditions in both Norfolk and Suffolk were bad but on the Continent they were considered to be the worst for 200 years. In Germany, the average temperature for February was the lowest since records began in 1766 and, in a number of Dutch cities, starving rats attacked feeding birds. Denmark and Sweden were linked by a solid sea of ice and hundreds of ships were stuck fast in the Baltic seaways.

Two years later, on 26th February, 1958, East Anglia was hit by an even greater snowstorm. It began on Tuesday with such suddenness that, within hours, villages were isolated, railway lines blocked and children stranded in schools. Norwich was cut off from surrounding districts and even snowploughs were abandoned.

Meteorologist, Mr J.H.Willis reported that nine inches of snow fell on the city, making it the worst blizzard for 50 years. By Wednesday, the two counties were so completely held in this icy grip that all main roads were blocked, all train services curtailed, all schools closed and all villages cut off from the outside world.

Helicopters came to the rescue, taking bread and essential supplies to numerous old folk's homes. At Lakenham, a large letter 'H' was etched in the snow to show the helicopter where it was safe to land. At Aylsham, Happisburgh and Walcott, where electricity was cut off, stores ran out of candles. One of the many errands of mercy the Norfolk police were asked to perform was to notify anxious parents that their children were being "put up" somewhere.

Two days later the thaw set in, the roads cleared, the railways opened and the children, delighted by their adventures, were able to return home.

North Norfolk News
The Norfolk Chronicle and Journal

. 457   FRIDAY, FEBRUARY 28, 1958   THREE

re abandoned for 24
dnesday. The steam
be dug out.

rgency
f new
main

f the struggle to keep
Holt and Sheringham
gas during the
res was told yesterday
the Eastern Gas Board
eral manager, Mr. W.

cy measures included
the retorts at Crome
the first use of a ma
aid last year to link u
Walsham, Mundesle,
ham and Holt.
n his statement, said:
Gas Works suppl
lly Sheringham where
ing works. The failure
ty supply on Tuesday
oduction at Cromer by
. This failure stopped
ompletely of the carbu

Secondary Modern
eringham is to be
lly next Friday by
loyle, Parliamentary
the Ministry of
The ceremony is due
rt at 11 a.m.

plant and also stopped
r to the works from our

The scene at
this

Vehi
bl

ALTHOUGH
good, the
ing blizzard al
Roads wer
exposed main
made parking
The weather
the 61 member
District Counci
monthly meetin
morning. As th
Holt councillors
H. W. Moulton,
Mr. G. J. Hubb
Highways Surv
arrived after an
the blizzard.
Visibility, the
minimum. One
he had switch
blown his hoote
Between Bod
they were held
20 cars stopped
plough eventua
but its task wa
vehicles being s
on the road.

Car

Another me
R.D.C. to arriv

The North Norfolk News on Friday 28th February, 1958. The blinding blizzard had completely blocked all roads in the county and gangs of men worked feverishly to clear the way and remove abandoned vehicles. There were other anxieties for the people of Cromer, Holt and Sheringham, where electricity failed and emergency measures were required to keep the three towns supplied with gas.

After a wonderful summer, heavy gales with wind speeds of almost 100 mph, swept across East Anglia on 14th November, 1959, following in the wake of fog and frost. Photograph shows a herring drifter coming into harbour at Great Yarmouth, after an unpleasant time in a turbulent North Sea.

No rain in Lowestoft for 57 days

The glorious summer of 1959

THE summer of 1959 was one of the sunniest of the century. On 5th July at Cromer, the temperature reached 34 C (93F) — the foretaste of a long, dry spell in which some places in eastern England had no rain from 14th August until 10th October.

Among them was sunny Lowestoft. Day after day the sun bore down from a cloudless sky and the people of Lowestoft, and those lucky enough to be on holiday there, enjoyed every one of those 57 memorable, rainless days.

The peak, of course, was mid-August — the heart of the holiday season — when the Lowestoft Carnival attracted so many onlookers that they queued six deep in the centre of the town to watch the procession. One week later the annual regatta drew 4,000 spectators to Nicholas Everitt Park. Chorus girls rehearsing in the hot house that was the Sparrows' Nest Theatre cooled off every morning in the sea and,

in front of another massive crowd, a 23-year-old daredevil called Rudi Omenkowsky made a 270-yard blindfold crossing on a tightrope high above Oulton Broad.

Not everyone was happy. On one day at Oulton Broad, 50 boats were turned away because the moorings were full. Hotels were also packed and many people were forced to sleep on the beach. Guest house landladies and hotel proprietors took bookings for 1960 and by September not a single chalet or beach hut was available for the following season.

Early October came with no end to the summer. People bathing in the sea would have seen work begin on the new £44,000 Corton sea wall. Lowestoft was still to the forefront in providing coastal defences.

The heatwave came to an end on 10th October and a few days later, 14 years of Labour domination in Lowestoft also ended, when a young Conservative candidate called Jim Prior wrested the parliamentary seat from Edward Evans.

The snowy, shivering sixties

1960: A wet year with nearly 35 inches (894mm) of rain at Lowestoft, or 50 per cent above the average. However, it was snow that hit the headlines in January with roads blocked in the Cromer - Sheringham area and massive drifts around Wells and Fakenham as a result of strong north-east winds. On 14th January, the mercury fell to a chilling 14F (-10C) at East Bergholt.

1961: St Valentine's Day was warm enough to melt even the frostiest heart as temperatures rose to 62F (17C) in the Thetford area. There was another heatwave in July, with 14.5 hours of sun on the beach at Lowestoft on Saturday 1st July when 92F (33C) was recorded at Mildenhall. Cooler weather spread southwards during the next few days and there was an air frost in the Breckland on the 6th.

1962: It was the coldest year since 1919 with some remarkably low temperatures during the early summer. On the 1st and 3rd June the mercury fell to 22F (-6C) at Santon Downham. This is the lowest temperature ever recorded in Britain during this month and is lower than 23F (-5C) recorded on the summit of Ben Nevis,the highest peak in Britain in June, 1903. Most places did not see a temperature much above 77F (25C).

1963: From 1659 there have been only two colder winters, that of 1683-4 and 1739-40. Places inland had snow on the ground throughout January and February and, in the vicinity of Newmarket, the ground was covered on 66 days, with temperatures falling below freezing on every day bar two at Wattisham. The lowest temperature ever recorded in Norfolk was measured at Santon Downham on the morning of 23rd January — a bitter -2F(-19C). Letters were written to national newspapers saying that the severe weather was due to the inclusion of centigrade in weather forecasts! At Southery, Norfolk a deluge brought 5.9 inches (150mm) of rain in three hours during thunderstorms on 6th June.

1964: A dry year over Britain with only 17.23 inches (440mm) of rain at Terrington St Clement. Norfolk had the distinction of recording the warmest temperature in the British Isles this year with 91F (33C) on 28th August at Cromer, yet it was below freezing near Brandon just three days later.

1965: The Terrington-Little London area south of the Wash had both summer and winter in March. On 3rd March the mercury fell to just 6F(-14C) but blue skies and brilliant sunshine sent the temperature up to 72F (22C) on the 29th, a case of March coming in like a polar bear and going out like a camel!

1966: The stage looked set for a severe winter with high pressure over Europe feeding in very cold air during January. On the 14th, Wattisham had a maximum of 28F (-2C) and frequent snow showers gave a depth of four inches at Lowestoft on the 17th. By the 19th the mercury had sunk to 7F(-14C) in the vicinity of Norwich. On the 20th a blizzard threatened but instead of snow, freezing rain fell, followed by a thaw. The mercury rose and the month ended with the temperature at 54F(12C). Violent gales on Sunday 27th March brought visibility almost to nil at Swaffham in what was described as a 'dust bowl storm'. Clouds of dust blew from fields and great drifts almost blocked roads at Narford. At Mundford a pall of dust swirled over the fens in gales reaching 80mph and motorists drove with their headlights on. King's Lynn was littered with fallen tiles and guttering.

1967: "He who doffs his coat in January puts it on again in May" is an old saw which came true this year, as the first three days of the month were cold with snow showers. There was frost at night. By the 11th winds from the Continent, rather than the Arctic, caused temperatures to soar to 78F(26C) at Brandon and many other places. At West Raynham, thunder was heard on 16 days in May and the storms led to rainfall being 2 times above the average.

1968: Another series of fen blows occurred on 1st February and 18th-20th March. Thousands of acres of surface peat, fertiliser and seeds were lifted from fields and carried into drainage dykes and the cost was put at £40 per acre. In what was a summerlike heatwave, Britain's hottest March temperature was recorded at Cromer and Santon Downham on the 29th with 77F(25C). September brought dramatic weather. Twice within the space of 96 hours the rain gauge at the Norfolk Agricultural Station at Sprowston broke its September record. On the 11th, 1.56inches (40mm) fell and roads became awash in the Thorpe End area and throughout the Norwich area, with manhole covers forced into the air by the pressure of water.

1969: Following an extremely wet May, with rainfall 2 times the average, East Anglian farmers were hampered by wet fields and an estimated 80,000 acres intended for cropping had not been planted. One farmer sowed barley by dropping seed from an aircraft. August was very dull, with less than four hours of sun a day, the least sunshine since records began at Mildenhall in 1936. What a change in the early autumn weather. During September and October only 0.27 inches (7mm) of rain fell at Morely St Botolph and the temperature reached nearly 80F(27C) at East Dereham on 9th October.

The coldest winter since 1740

Christmas 1962 — March 1963

FROZEN rivers, ice floes at sea, deep snow from Christmas to March. This was the coldest winter since 1740 and it brought the most extraordinary arctic scenes to Norfolk and Suffolk. An unremitting easterly wind kept the mercury well below freezing for much of the winter but, in most people's memories, it was Boxing Day 1962 that ushered in the winter. From a steel grey sky the first flakes fell during the early afternoon and then quickly covered the countryside in a deep, silent blanket that was to last for weeks.

The first outriders of winter had already made their appearance in November, for at Sprowston, near Norwich, there were four days when snow lay. At Santon Downham, the temperature fell to 18F(-8C) on the 23rd. It was in December that winter began to tighten its grip with a foggy cold spell during the first week when the thermometer dropped to 14F (-10C) at East Bergholt. For a short time it became milder but a plunge of arctic air on the 12th shrouded parts of Norfolk in two inches of snow.

By Christmas Day the air was cold and still and an area of rain over Scotland turned to snow as it reached East Anglia on Boxing Day. Slowly it fell, flake upon flake, muffling the countryside and, as the skies cleared, a bitterly cold 9F (-13C) was recorded at Mildenhall on the 29th.

Worse was to follow. An area of low pressure gathered strength in the southwest approaches and unleashed a blizzard of fine powdery snow across the southern half of Britain on the 29th December. Huge drifts, whipped up by gale-force winds, were created. Nationwide, more than 95,000 miles of highway became snowbound. Conditions in Woodbridge typified events all over East Anglia. A motorist on his way to Kettleburgh and Easton became incarcerated in a 10-foot drift near Eyke. He dug his way through a wall of snow about four feet high and 30 feet long, only to find an even bigger drift further down the road. It took a tractor nearly an hour to pull out his van.

At Wickham Market snow towered 12 feet on the side of the road. All roads to Haverhill were blocked. It took some improvisation at RAF Honington to keep the airport open. They mounted jet engines on a trolley and the exhaust blast cleared a six foot wide path through the snow.

After signs of a thaw proved short lived early in the month, January brought persistent easterly winds which continued to drift the snow. In the Dereham area alone, five big ploughs and 40 smaller ones assisted by six diggers battled unceasingly. It was impossible for any traffic to reach Shipdham on the A1075. Bus drivers were issued with spades before taking out their vehicles.

Roads were blocked not only by snow but also by soil. Winds gusting to more than 60 mph on the 19th cleared the snow on exposed fields and then removed the top soil. At the height of the gale visibility at Weybourne was just a few yards as the air was filled with choking dust and soil. At Loddon, the dust clouds were estimated to be 200 feet high and roads were a foot deep in soil.

On the coast icicles adorned Gorleston pier and, in more sheltered places, 40 foot ice-floes stopped the ferry services to Bawdsey. At Oulton Broad, the ice was thick enough to hold its skating championship over a mile-long course but a 45lb lamb, roasted on its frozen surface, had to be taken ashore quickly. Charcoal was melting the ice.

Later in the month the winds dropped but the cold intensified and Norfolk's coldest ever temperature was recorded early on the 23rd with a numbing -2F (-19C) at Santon Downham and 4F (-15C) at Mildenhall This caused pipes to freeze and water supplies were severed at Ipswich. The supply also failed at the Atomic Energy Establishment at Orford Ness. Water was brought in by barge for four days and tankers supplied householders with this vital commodity.

Sugar beet remained unharvested and, what hadn't been raided by rats, rabbits and birds, had to be released by pickaxe, as did bales of straw in Swilland. In many places, soil froze to a depth of seven inches.

With high pressure situated over East Anglia, light winds and clear skies led to dense, freezing fog and when it cleared the landscape was a fairyland scene with thick rime deposited on trees and shrubs, almost an inch thick in Bury St Edmunds.

Bird life suffered considerably. Teal, shoveller duck and mallard dropped to a tenth of their population whereas shelduck feeding on unfrozen tidal mud were present in greater numbers. Oysters were decimated at Orford with losses between 30 and 60 per cent. On land, hares and rabbits turned to furze and bark for food.

The severe conditions continued in February with air frost on every night at West Raynham. A measure of the intensity of cold was reflected in its average temperature for the whole winter — 30.5F (-0.5C). Snow lay for 60 days, a situation more common in Poland than East Anglia.

Nature, after gripping the countryside in icy tentacles for week after week did at least release its hold gradually. There was no storm-lashed thaw, as in 1947, when floodwaters took the place of snow. The sun shone and, as February passed into March, daytime temperatures rose to 41F (5C). By 6th March, Cromer enjoyed a balmy 61F (16C). Fields and lawns were visible again. Spring was on its way.

We've heard of having ice with your drink, but wasn't this taking it a little far! A photograph to illustrate that it was an exceptionally cold winter was taken by the Eastern Daily Press on the frozen Wensum in Norwich in January 1963

Frozen sea at Heacham, Norfolk in January 1963.

The River Deben was frozen during the winter of 1963, and again in 1985 when this picture was taken by Mrs Olive Hopwood of Melton.

The sea around the pier at Hunstanton as it looked in January, 1963.

The King's Lynn Pelicans are a hockey team of some renown. In February 1963, when the water in the New Cut froze, a few enthusiasts cleared away the snow on the river and organised an ice hockey match. One member, David Whitmore, said: "The ice was on the water from Boxing Day right through to March and when one of the heavy buoys went through it, I measured the thickness — 18 inches".

LEFT: In a one horse open sleigh. Mrs Sally Walrond enjoys a bracing ride in the 100-year-old Russian sleigh in the Shimpling district, Bury St Edmunds, in January 1963. Zapateado provided the horse-power.

The memories of this amazing winter are very clear. Robert Helyer of Langham, near Bury remembers the "Tonight" television programme being broadcast from Oulton Broad, when presenter Cliff Michelmore had a desk on the ice and was surrounded by his camera crew. During the programme they cut a hole in the ice and it was 10 inches thick.

BELOW: Ice coats the rail of the German Fisheries Research Vessel, "Anton Dohrn", arriving at Yarmouth. It completed its crossing of the North Sea on 23rd January, 1963.

The scene at Orford on 19th November 1963, showing some of the damage caused by the surprise whirlwind. Here, firemen are carrying out emergency repairs to the roof of the village inn, The Jolly Sailor, which was badly damaged.

Just like Hurricane Flora!

19th November, 1963

A whirlwind, which swept across the marshes, struck the Suffolk village of Orford so violently that chimney stacks were hurled to the ground, telephone wires torn down, tiles smashed and roads blocked by fallen trees. One moment there was a normal November breeze blowing through the village and the next there was utter confusion as this rare weather phenomenon struck with awesome power. It lasted just 15 minutes.

Orford was the worst hit but the whole of east Suffolk suffered as blinding rain and hail flooded roads and forced motorists to abandon their journeys. It was particularly bad at Sudbury, Haverhill, Great Thurlow, Withersfield, Castle Camps, Little Wratting, Wixoe and Baythorne.

Mr and Mrs Sidney Harper of The Jolly Sailor Inn in Quay Street, Orford had a remarkable escape from injury when their house, which backs onto the marshes, caught the full fury of the storm. Within a few minutes, three big chimneys at the inn crashed down on to the roof and brickwork, tiles and timber were hurled on to the road.

Quay Street was completely blocked. Orford Fire Brigade, workmen of East Suffolk Council Roads and Bridges Department, Post Office engineers and volunteers spent the rest of the day clearing rubble and reconnecting services. Mr Harper said: "If we had been in the road at the time we would have died. It reminded me of Hurricane Flora".

Storm clouds gather above the Broads.

Spanish dust falls on East Anglia

1st July, 1968

MOTORISTS were mystified, housewives were harassed and farmers were fuming. Their cars, their houses and their crops were covered by a dirty-looking powdery substance which had fallen from the sky across an area from the Fens to the coast. No-one, it seems, had experienced this phenomenon before or could explain it.

The "dirty rain", as it was called, fell on Sunday 1st July, 1968 around 6 pm with a repeat performance early on the Monday morning. First reports came from motorists in Norwich and Ipswich who noticed the residual dust on their vehicles.

By mid-day hundreds of alarmed reports were received by newspapers, police stations and council offices. Was this a fall-out from a nuclear explosion ? Was it radio-active dust? What were the county health departments doing about it ? People even asked if it was anything to do with the sulphur-burning chimney at Bacton. They were told this was not yet built.

The Meteorological Office at Bracknell supplied the answer. The "dirty rain" was the result of thunderstorms in the Bay of Biscay which had originated in Spain or Morocco and were now moving up through England. The air where these storms came from was dusty and the soil very dry. This accounted for the deposits, said the Met Office. They were now collecting samples for analysis.

London Weather Centre agreed. The phenomenon was most unusual but not unkown. During the recent high winds, the dust was lifted into the upper atmosphere and carried around in convective clouds. It is a regular occurrence over parts of the Mediterranean but occurs in the British Isles about once in 15 years or so.

Throughout the week the effects of the dust storm continued to be a great talking point but the colours of the deposits differed. They were coloured red, brown, pink, yellow, white and orange. When told that, in the Norwich area, they were greyish, a spokesman from the London Weather Centre replied: "That's a new one".

From North Norfolk came reports of falling cement powder. From Yarmouth and Lowestoft, red brick deposits. From Taverham, a shower of honey-dew from limes and sycamore. From Wisbech, red rain. From Downham Market, a sub-tropical rainstorm and possibly a minor whirlwind.

On Monday evening, 2nd July, Anglian Water reported a considerable strain on water supplies as people washed the Spanish and Moroccan dust from their cars, clothes and homes.

It was on Saturday 14th September, 1968 that the wide skies of Norfolk turned grey, then black as low pressure deepened rapidly. The arrival of this weather system was heralded by a spectacular storm and then incessant rain throughout the following day.

Wild waters of September 1968

Deluge of tropical intensity

THIS was the storm to rival the greatest of the twentieth century. In Ipswich and Suffolk they compared it to the horror storm of 1939; in Norwich and Norfolk, older people looked back to the great deluge of 1912. On this September day in 1968, lightning flashed, thunder rolled and the rain fell in torrents. Hour after hour the great black chasm above released its load in proportions of tropical intensity.

By the following day, Monday, valleys, towns, villages and hamlets were under water. Rivers burst their banks, landslides blocked roads and railways and huge lakes spread out over hundreds of acres of low-lying land. Vehicles floated away and so did livestock. Helicopters were employed to rescue people in distress and all available police were called on duty to deal with the emergency.

The culprit had been a rapidly deepening area of low pressure to the south-west of Britain which produced a pronounced 'trough' across to the south east, along which there were large-scale vertical motions of the atmosphere. It remained stationary all day on 15th September and that meant prolonged heavy rain.

In Suffolk, the towns of Beccles and Bungay were completely cut off. The main road was flooded to a depth of four feet and there was a landslide on the embankment at Halesworth station. At Halesworth, floodwater poured through the main shopping centre in the Thoroughfare. It slopped against doors and windows, found a way into every shop and caused thousands of pounds worth of damage. The printing works of the Halesworth Press were flooded and all power cut off. People were taken from one end of the Thoroughfare to the other in a small boat by the manager of Lloyds Bank. Sandbags were rushed to the town centre and stranded people slept in the lounge and bar of the Angel Hotel.

The gushing water tore a huge gap in the railway embankment beside the bridge over Holton Road. The main street of Holton village was flooded for several hundred yards. At nearby Wissett, a car descending the hill into the village, ran into a great wall of water. The force of the raging torrent carried the car downstream where it came to stop by a low-brick wall. All five occupants were rescued.

The rivers of Suffolk could not cope with the sheer

Most of Bury was without power until Tuesday morning, 18th September, for an electrical transformer in the aptly named Raingate Street was awash. Here Eastern Electricity engineers ferry equipment down Baker's Lane in a hastily prepared raft. The picture was taken near the Rushbrook Arms, where the River Lark runs under the A134.

speed and weight of the water. Worst hit was the main A1120 Yoxford to Stowmarket Road which was inundated near Peasenhall primary school. The Leiston to Sizewell Road, the only one leading to the nuclear power station, was also flooded. At Saxmundham water poured into the police and the bus stations.

Many motorists in the Beccles area became marooned as the great brown floods surrounded them. They included an *East Anglian Daily Times* reporter and his wife, Mr and Mrs J.S.Kirby. At Brampton Corner at the junction with Beccles, Southwold and Halesworth Roads they abandoned their car and waded waist high through the water with the rain still pounding down. They climbed onto higher ground and were rescued by the driver of a Blythburgh Hospital van.

In the north of the county the A12 was impassable in many places.

The situation in West Suffolk was chaotic. Bury St Edmunds, Haverhill and numerous villages were cut off by floods and army units with amphibious vehicles helped police and firemen to evacuate stranded people. In many streets, cars and buses were replaced by boats, dinghies and rafts.

The village of Long Melford was breached at both ends of the main street and six cottages in Southgate Street were flooded as water came up from the riverside meadows. The level of the river at Ballingdon Bridge, Sudbury was so high that the borough organised an all-night vigil for fear the town would be completely swamped. As it was, Sudbury was surrounded by a massive flood half a mile across. Cavendish and Glemsford were also cut off and an elderly lady was one of many inhabitants rescued from their homes where water was five feet deep.

There were other dramatic rescues. On Monday, 16th September, a pregnant woman was airlifted by helicopter to hospital from her flooded home in Haverhill. She gave birth the following day. A policeman swam through the swirling waters to rescue a mother and two children in Sicklesmere. A 14-year-old Convent girl dived into the swollen waters to rescue a horse in Bury.

The main Ipswich-Norwich line was blocked when a bridge, north of Diss, was swept away. Here, possible tragedy was averted by a Norfolk farmer who was tending his cattle alongside the line when

An aerial view of Loddon, taken by an Eastern Evening News photographer, who flew over the flood area.

he heard the bridge collapse. Peter Young of Walton Green Farm, Burston walked down the line until he came to a telephone which connected him to a signalman. He gave the alarm and all trains on the line were halted. The main line between Cambridge and Ipswich was also closed when an archway under a bridge at Kentford disappeared with the floodwater and the railway track was seen hanging over a gaping hole.

In Norfolk, the rainfall during the 24-hour period from 10 am on Sunday 15th measured 4.5 inches at Shotesham, 2.36 inches at Yarmouth, 2.83 inches at Old Lakenham — the most in one day since the great deluge of 1912.

Every road out of Norwich, except the A11 was either completely blocked or badly flooded. Rivers burst their banks and millions of gallons of storm water filled dykes, broads and reservoirs. A county wide alert went out for reinforcements as firemen began to pump water out from basements and shop cellars in many towns. An emergency road-weather centre was set up by the AA who began their warning by advising motorists not to venture near Attleborough or Old Buckenham where the River Tas was flowing four-feet deep down the main road.

It was the same story in many parts of the county. This extraordinary deluge caused thousands of pounds worth of damage but no-one suffered more than the farmers whose unharvested wheat crop was completely ruined.

Vehicles, partly submerged, on the road between Haverhill and Sudbury, in the Stour valley. This was the extraordinary sight on Monday morning 16th September, 1968.

An aerial view of Bungay showing some of the area flooded by the great deluge of 16th September, 1968.

An aerial view of flood damage to the main Ipswich to Norwich railway line at Burston, near Diss. Here, a local farmer prevented a possible major catastrophe.

Walsham-le-Willows was invaded by the swirling brown flood waters.

CHAPTER TEN: 1970 — 1979

A survey of the seventies

1970: There were 107 hours of sun at Terrington St Clement in February, one of the sunniest Februarys of the century. Only 0.2 inches (5mm) of rain fell in the King's Lynn area in May. On 3rd June water spouts were seen in the Wash. Most parts had a traditional Christmas with snow showers carpeting the ground on Christmas Day.

1971: During a cold first week of March, the mercury fell to 11F (-11.7C) at Santon Downham on the 5th. In July, Gorleston recorded 3.45 inches (88mm) of rain in 24 hours on the 28th and Great Yarmouth suffered heavy flooding, while on 7th August a violent whirlwind led to over £10,000 of damage to crops and farm buildings at Haverhill.

1972: In a mild winter there was a brief burst of bitter cold when high pressure established itself over Scandinavia and produced a surge of icy air from the east. On 31st January the temperature did not exceed 21F(-6C) at Cromer but early February brought mild air in from the Atlantic. 1st August brought cool northerly winds and, with cold air aloft over East Anglia, conditions were ripe for severe storms. On this day 5.51 inches (141mm) of rain fell at Old Costessey, Norwich, most of it in just two hours and there was a tornado at Ipswich.

1973: On Monday 2nd April a small but intense low pressure area moved east across the Midlands and severe gales blew in Norfolk and Suffolk. Just after 2pm a gust of 76mph occurred at West Raynham. A 30-ton pine tree fell and killed two men at Scoulton. There were 50 reports from Suffolk of trees blocking roads and there was a dramatic rescue of the crew from the 1900-ton m.v. *Amberley* by three RAF helicopters as it drifted without its steerage off Cromer. One sad victim of the storm was the huge old cedar tree associated with nurse Edith Cavell at Swardeston. It was under that tree that she received, on a sunny July day, a telegram calling her back to Belgium, never to see England again.

1974: January was the warmest since 1932 and December since 1934, the latter having no air frost at Downham Market and Great Barton when dahlias were in bloom and snowdrops in flower. There was no lying snow in many parts during the year. According to one weather observer in Norwich, the spring was the driest since 1839, when records started. The East Anglian Water Authority toured north Norfolk with 'loudhailer' vans urging people to economise. This was followed by a ban on hosepipes. Local farmers prayed for rain and they were answered.

1975: Another mild January but a cool spring. There were snowflakes five inches across near King's Lynn on 30th March. An exceptional plunge of cold arctic air on 2nd June gave snow in many places and it lay briefly at Elmswell in Suffolk. Yet, just over a week later, the temperature reached 82F (28C) and continued warm through the summer. Indeed it never dropped below 70F(21C) at Wattisham on the night of 4th-5th August. There were heavy thunderstorms and one offshore struck the Shell 48B platform, igniting waste gases and sending flames into the sky on July 17th, whilst at Aylsham 4.75 inches(120mm) of rain fell in two hours.

1976: An eventful year began with a severe storm on the evening of 2nd January when a rapidly deepening depression crossed Scotland. Winds gusted to 103mph at Norwich and 104mph at Cromer. The summer provided drought and great heat with 94F(34C) at Scole on 26th June. Rainfall from August 1975 to July 1976 was only 14.3 inches, around 60 per cent of normal at King's Lynn. Underground water supplies from chalk aquifers fell to record levels in Norfolk. Due to water restrictions a nude swimming scene in the production "PyjamaTops" at Ipswich had to be cancelled. Naked badminton players were substituted.

1977: Parts of Norfolk had another dry spell with less rain falling from mid-May to the end of August at Buxton than during the drought summer of the previous year. Top soil was blown from fields causing large drifts against hedges on 20th May. Grass withered, sugar beet and wheat suffered though with much lower temperatures and cloudier skies the drought was less severe. There were some severe storms and one at Ipswich on 8th August gave 1.39 inches(36mm) in an hour.

1978: A tornado at Newmarket on 3rd January as cold air pushing away mild air wreaked havoc along a 70 yard swathe. Meanwhile a vicious depression travelling east across England brought a furious gale on 11th, sweeping away most of Hunstanton's pier. There were severe thunderstorms on 30th July with many trees damaged by lightning at Dereham. Hailstones were nearly an inch across at Coltishall, with 2.4 inches (60mm) of rain at Tittleshall.

1979: January was the coldest since 1963 with the temperature down to just 1F(-17C) at Sculthorpe, Norfolk on the night of 27th/28th. Snow was up to a foot deep in parts of East Anglia in February and 200 stranded motorists spent the night at The Guildhall, Bury St Edmunds. Many roads were blocked.

Just like the ones I used to know!

25th December, 1970

AS children slept and Santa Claus was at his busiest, the counties of Norfolk and Suffolk were being transformed into a great white winter wonderland. Christmas Day, 1970 was a classic white Christmas. Several inches had fallen overnight and the words of the most famous festive song had come true at last.

Although snow had fallen on Boxing Day in 1962 and 1968, parents struggled to remember "the ones we used to know". The last white Christmas in East Anglia was 1938 and before that, 1927 and 1923. In fact, only one other in 1906, had occurred since the turn of the century.

There had been a few more white Christmases in the nineteenth century, including one in 1870, exactly 100 years earlier, when the temperature plunged to 23F (-5C) and there was a deep fall of snow.

As recounted on an earlier page, Charles Dickens, born 1812, described a white Christmas at Dingley Dell in his book *Pickwick Papers*. He was probably influenced by some very real memories in his early teens when there was a one in four chance of snow lying on at least two of the three Christmas days.

The most likely white Christmases were those prior to the reform of the calendar in 1752 — and that is where the legend really comes from. Christmas then fell on what is now 6th January — and, of course, there has always been much more snow around in the first two weeks of January than the last two in December.

The criteria for a white Christmas is that snow must fall and settle on Christmas Day. Seldom are they local affairs, for snow at this time of the year invariably involves much of the country and is part of a broad pattern extending over much of Scandinavia and the Continent.

So when grandad declares that white Christmases were the rule rather than the exception when he was a child, then his memory is playing tricks. The table below shows the dates of the "classics" and the near misses.

WHITE CHRISTMASES IN EAST ANGLIA

1906 Several inches

1923 Snow in Norfolk

1927 Typical snowstorm

1938 Snow fell every day from 15th December

1970 Between four and eight inches

Some slight falls occurred in 1917 and 1956.
In 1981, snow lay several inches deep but it had fallen before Christmas Day which was sunny with blue skies

Snow in June, 1975

The first recorded authentic June snowfall in East Anglia occurred on 2nd June, 1975. The *Evening Star* wrote: "Freezing levels were at abnormally low altitudes and there followed the greatest southward penetration of June snow in Great Britain for 87 years".

Some miles further south, in Colchester, Essex, a county cricket match between Essex and Kent was halted because of the snow. Anglia TV weatherman Michael Hunt said at the time that he had no record of snow in June south of The Wash in the 20th century. He blamed the persistent high pressure to the north of the British Isles for causing the icy winds.

The snow did not last long. By 12th June, Ipswich and Suffolk were basking in temperatures in the upper 70's. There followed a long, hot vintage summer, in which temperatures climbed into the 80's on 7th August and the next day reached the dizzy heights of 93F (34C) at Marham, Norfolk.

Many people had difficulty in sleeping at night because of the stuffy conditions. At the time it was widely regarded as being on a par with 1947 which had provided the warmest weather in 300 years.

But then came the summer of 1976...

600 trees topple in Norwich

2nd-3rd January, 1976

THIS was the Big One that East Anglia had been bracing itself for — a storm surge that had much in common with 1953. It occurred on a Friday evening, the sea hammering coastal defences from The Wash to Felixstowe, destroying chalets, cutting off three lifeboats and ripping large holes in concrete sea defences and promenades. The flood warning system worked well; families living in vulnerable places along the coast had been evacuated several hours before high water and there was no loss of life. The difference, on this occasion, was that the really high tidal surge expected in the wake of the gales never came and a repetition of the 1953 disaster was averted.

After a week of stormy weather, a depression moved across Scotland into the North Sea. During the night of 2nd-3rd January, 1976 it deepened so suddenly that winds of hurricane force or more hurled themselves at the eastern counties. By daybreak, Norfolk and Suffolk were reeling from a storm which had devastated homes, crippled communications and gave the new coastal defences their first real test.

Every town and village in the two counties suffered but Norwich bore the brunt of this assault. By 11 o'clock, all roads out of the city were blocked and, in the city itself, more than 600 trees were blown down as the winds gusted at up to 102 mph. The Bury to Thetford Road was blocked for more than six hours and it was estimated that 300 forestry trees were brought down at Newmarket. There was considerable damage in Ipswich, Sudbury, Haverhill, Fakenham and Aylsham.

Electricity supplies also failed, affecting 100,000 consumers. Almost half of these spent two days without power. A Blaxall man was electrocuted when he touched a high tension cable brought down by a tree, and a girl from Cockfield, near Bury, was seriously hurt when a tree collapsed on top of her.

As the storm-lashed counties assessed the cost of the havoc there was brighter news from the coastal communities. Flooding and damage was widespread but the defences, which had cost millions of pounds, held — a fact which delighted Anglian Water who had been at the forefront of the reconstruction work.

The exception was at Walcott in Norfolk where the new wall collapsed in more than 12 places, the sea broke through and more than 150 people had to be evacuated. The RAF, with dryers, and the fire brigade, with pumping equipment, quickly moved into the village. At Caister, great holes were torn in the wall, doubling the cost of a scheme to strengthen it.

At King's Lynn, the Great Ouse reached a height of 29 feet at the peak of the tide. Some quays were flooded and Nelson Street, in one of the oldest parts of the town, was swamped by water forced up from the drains. The sea also broke through at Blakeney and the shingle bank, which still remained as the sole defence of Salthouse against the North Sea, was breached. The high tides rose six feet above their predicted levels at Great Yarmouth but there was only minor flooding because of the protective walls of the River Yare. There was some confusion and concern at Lowestoft, owing to a rumour that tides were two hours behind normal. High tide came dead on time and the worst damage was to beach chalets along the promenade which were swept away to sea.

Beccles and Stowmarket were badly affected. The River Yare overflowed at Beccles, flooding the yacht station and adjacent Fen Lane. Homes were protected by a barrier of sandbags and residents stayed up until 2 am anxiously waiting for the water to subside. At Wetherden, near Stowmarket, a three ton chimney caved into the Maypole public house but tenants and customers escaped injury. Elsewhere, there were serious inundations at St Olaves, Shingle Street, Potters Bridge and Blackmore, where the Harbour Inn was flooded to a depth of five feet. Here, a landing stage was swept upriver to Blythburgh. The Walberswick marshes were flooded over an area of several miles and residents were rescued by villagers in rowing boats. The harbour master said it was the most water he had ever seen.

At Southwold, it was touch and go on Friday night whether to evacuate or not but eventually it proved unnecessary. It was the same story at Aldeburgh, where doors and windows were barricaded, as the sea crashed dramatically against the new sea wall. A full alert went out, but Aldeburgh remained unscathed.

Emergency procedures were also in place at Felixstowe where tides reached exceptional heights. Police toured the Langer Road, Manor Terrace and seafront areas with loud hailers warning people to prepare to leave their homes. The horrors of 1953 would certainly have been on their minds as residents of Felixstowe, on this January night, waited for the danger to pass.

The *Eastern Evening News* reported one "terrible tragedy" at the Black Lion, the Buxtons, near Aylsham where trees blew down blocking all exit roads from the pub, just at closing time. The locals were faced with an awful dilemma — whether to walk home in the teeth of a "hurricane" or stay on in the warmth and comfort of the Black Lion.

Who said it's an ill wind?

Beach huts at Wells could not withstand the maelstrom.

A blocked road at North Wootton Church, King's Lynn — but the post gets through. This was Monday 5th January 1976.

East Anglia wilts in the sunshine

Blazing summer of 1976

THERE had never been a summer like it — a summer of barbecues, bikinis, blazing sun, blazing countryside and bad cases of sunburn. As Norfolk and Suffolk sizzled and everyone rushed for the beach, the weathermen rushed for their record books. For 16 successive days the temperature somewhere in England reached, or exceeded 90F (32C), an unprecedented event.

There were massive crowds in resorts all over East Anglia, particularly in June, July and August. During these months, Cromer, Hunstanton, Great Yarmouth, Lowestoft and Felixstowe enjoyed record hours of sunshine and the sea temperatures were among the highest ever recorded.

With much of the area receiving less than 60 per cent of its average rainfall between May 1975 and August 1976, this represented the worst drought since 1921. Holidaymakers may have loved it but the continuing heatwave threatened industry and worried the Government into appointing a Minister of Drought and applying the most stringent restrictions. The people of East Anglia were even advised to put a brick in the cistern and take a bath with a friend.

On 24th June the temperature in Felixstowe climbed to 92F (33C) and the "bucket and spade" brigade sent traffic figures soaring. Local police dished out more than 100 parking tickets and said it was the busiest day they had ever known on the beach. It was the start of an extraordinary week in which the temperatures in London reached 95F (35C) on the 26th and many parts of the country experienced their hottest June night for 29 years.

As weathermen predicted continuing heatwaves, a Suffolk doctor advocated a pint and a packet of crisps as the best way of replacing the liquid and salt that was being lost. His advice came as the county's ambulancemen were coping with up to 120 emergency calls a day.

Norfolk and Suffolk became tinder dry. Fires broke out on heathland, farmland and forest. Day after day there were hundreds of calls for assistance, straining the resources of the county brigade. On one occasion 60 firemen, using nine appliances, battled in scorching weather to control a grass fire that swept through a lane of bungalows and houses in King's Lynn. The fire was caused by a cigarette carelessly thrown from a vehicle on the King's Lynn by-pass. Divisional Commander of the Norfolk Fire Service, Donald West said: "We are reaching exhaustion stage, our service is stretched to the limit and the attitude of the public is one of total indifference."

During the first week in July, there were more than 350 calls for assistance, which brought an urgent appeal for extra vigilance in Norfolk where thousands of acres of standing crops were threatened. Two days later, a square mile of corn at Corpusty, near the road from Norwich to Holt went up in flames and the hard-pressed firemen needed help from police, passers-by and farm workers in controlling the blaze.

Anglian Water banned the use of hoses and sprinklers for the first time since 1947. Householders were advised to water their gardens with bath water and Draconian penalties were introduced for anyone found defying the ban. Divisional water engineers in both counties told householders to look out for water hogs and it was estimated that those who ignored the restrictions were using up to 220 gallons a day on baths, toilets, dishwashers, washing machines and garden sprinklers.

The ban did not apply to golf courses and public gardens and resentment grew. At Dereham Golf Course, in July, the hoses supplying the sprinklers on the green were cut through and the local police received anonymous calls. In Norwich, there were angry protests to the city council as tennis courts, bowling greens and gardens continued to be watered. A spokesman said the Corporation was exercising great restraint but warned that it would cost a lot of money if the city's greens and courts had to be ploughed up and relaid, through lack of water.

As August arrived with no sign of a break in the weather, the Government became even more concerned about the potentially disastrous water situation. Reservoirs were dangerously low and in some places their clay bottoms were cracking in the heat. Discolouration of the water was also affecting many areas and for some days the people of Hellesdon had no water at all, as engineers worked furiously to line the water pipes with bitumen paint.

On 20th August, the Norfolk Agricultural Station at Morely, near Wymondham reported that it had had no measurable rain for 17 days and the county was in the middle of its third drought of the year. The Government then played its trump card. Denis Howell was appointed Minister of Drought and, as he took office, the persistent block of high pressure broke down and East Anglia enjoyed heavy rain.

September, 1976 was one of the wettest months ever known.

Dave Kindred of The East Anglian Daily Times took this picture of Nicole, aged four, following the advice on the notice board as she prepared for a game of tennis on another balmy day in early September, 1976.

TEN WONDERFUL EAST ANGLIAN SUMMERS

1911: A long hot summer with 1,942 hours of sun in Ipswich during the year. Temperature of 96F at Bury St Edmunds.

1921: Driest year of the century. Nearly 1,800 hours of sun in Norwich.

1933: Norwich enjoyed 706 hours of sunshine during June to August —nearly eight hours a day.

1947: A Mediterranean-like summer. August's average maximum value was nearly 78F (25.6C).

1949: Summer started early with temperatures up to 80F in mid-April and the upper 80's as late as September.

1959: Cromer's weather station recorded 93F (34C) on 5th July and Lowestoft had 57 successive rainless days in a summer that continued into early October when Mildenhall recorded 82F (28C).

1975: At Scole, daytime temperatures averaged 78F (25.5C) in August but the summer began with snow on 2nd June!

1976: In June, Cromer averaged 10.3 hours of sun a day and the mercury approached 96F (35.5C) at East Dereham. In July, Cromer broke its sunshine record with 318 hours.

1989: At Beccles there was a princely 1,933 hours of sun this year which began in May with more than 300 hours of sunshine

1990: It was the sunniest year on record in parts of East Anglia, reaching almost 2,000 hours. In August temperatures peaked at around 93F (34C). Every day in August approached, or exceeded 70F (21C).

Holidaymakers on the Broads in 1976. In June, there were almost 300 hours of sunshine.

Norwich came to a standstill on the evening of 14th January, 1977 as a huge snowstorm swept the city. Within hours nearly every road was blocked by slithering, skidding vehicles. Snowploughs and gritting lorries were trapped in the most chaotic conditions seen for years. Buses were paralysed, the airport was closed, telephone wires collapsed and, on the coast, lifeboats stood by to rescue fishermen in distress. In the picture pedestrians and motorists were fighting their way home along Rampant Horse Street.

The path of the whirlwind. A fence and a section of roof were damaged and just tossed aside.

The Newmarket whirlwind

5th January, 1978

A destructive whirlwind ripped through the racing town of Newmarket days after the 1978 New Year celebrations. The morning rush hour of Tuesday 5th January was coming to a close when a roaring wind, hell-bent on causing maximum damage, seemed to spring up from nowhere.

Within minutes, cars had been overturned, roofs lifted off and sheds blown sky high. People were knocked off their feet and vehicles were forced off roads. A four-mile trail of damage was caused before the rotating storm expended all its pent-up energy.

Eye witnesses saw debris hurtling through the air at roof-top height. Considering the amount of people that were out and about, it was remarkable that no-one was killed, but several people suffered minor injuries. One of the worst-hit places was the Coronation Hotel where landlord Vin Waterfall was knocked off his feet by the blast. The wind lifted tiles off the hotel roof and masonry fell into the car park.

The whirlwind struck at 9.15 am. It came from the direction of Newmarket Heath and left a trail of damage across Hamilton Road, Tattersalls' sales paddocks, Crockfords Park estate, Duchess Drive and Centre Drive before moving onto Ashley. It lasted little more than a minute.

The signal box at Newmarket Station was wrecked and the signalman, Peter Greco of Mildenhall, was treated for shock. Outside, his car was overturned. Commuters arrived home later to find a scene resembling the aftermath of a riot. Windscreens were smashed and concrete posts in the car park were bent over by the force of the wind.

Striking firemen at Newmarket abandoned their dispute to answer calls for help. Mr William Crump from Bungay was taken to hospital after his car was blown from the road. Peggy Halford of Ashley suffered shoulder injuries when her garage door was torn off its hinges. Miss Constance Viall's garage was completely demolished.

The revolving storm was triggered by an active cold front moving quickly across the country bringing a sharp drop in temperature and a sudden change in wind direction. The whirlwind kept to a narrow path less than 100 yards wide and moved in a straight line from the Heath to Ashley.

The car, the signalbox and the signalman, Peter Greco, were in the way of the Newmarket whirlwind. He was treated in hospital for shock.

Tragedy on land and sea

11th January, 1978

THERE was unlikely to be a repetition of the 1976 storm for many years, said the experts. Gales of this ferocity occur only once or twice in a lifetime. Two years later, almost to the day, Norfolk and Suffolk were looking at damage running into tens of thousands of pounds after heavy seas, gale-force winds and huge spring tides had combined to show a malevolent hand yet again.

The symptoms were the same. A rapidly deepening depression which moved across England towards the Netherlands with severe northerly gales developing behind it. On this occasion, however, the low pressure also caused a tidal surge — even bigger than that of 1953. As in 1976 the sea defences held firm but in many places they were overtopped by mountainous waves, bringing chaos in their wake.

The greatest dramas on this night of ferment were at sea. The Wisbech-bound, Greek coaster *Sea Diamond*, carrying a cargo of salt put out a Mayday call just before midnight on Wednesday 11th January. As conditions worsened rapidly in 80 mph winds and nothing more was heard, three lifeboats from Caister, Gorleston and Lowestoft were launched, in what coastguards described as "really atrocious conditions", and began a widespread search.

The coaster was found two miles off Lowestoft but the seven-man crew was gone. One by one the bodies were recovered — one had been carried 20 miles by the gale-force winds to a point three miles off Aldeburgh. The lifeboats had been joined in the search by an RAF Nimrod helicopter, a USAF Hercules and the frigate, HMS *Jupiter*. Conditions were worse than anyone could remember.

Another ship out at sea on this wild night was the Townsend Thorensen ferry, *Viking Voyager*, attempting the journey from Zeebrugge to Felixstowe with cars, freight and passengers. After an ordeal lasting 12 hours in a force 12 gale, the ferry berthed undamaged and the grateful passengers came ashore to tell their harrowing tale. In the ferry port itself the sea came over the jetty, flooding the car park and dragging five boats from their moorings. Again, the people of Felixstowe prepared to abandon their homes and a school in the town was opened to receive the evacuees. The wall held and the danger passed.

Damage amounting to thousands of pounds was caused at Southwold where the North Pier was battered by tumultuous waves causing the seaward wall of the amusement arcade to collapse. The old pier survived but, elsewhere on the east coast, the piers at Hunstanton, Walton-on-the Naze, Margate and Herne Bay were reduced to piles of contorted girders and matchwood.

Inland, there was flooding at Beccles, Bungay, Stowmarket, Needham Market and Waldringfield, on the River Deben, where a 30-foot yacht was holed and sunk and a dinghy found hooked up in a tree, three miles inland.

In storm-scarred Norfolk three people were killed. Two died at Morton-on-the-Hill after a car swerved to avoid a branch in the road and was in collision with a lorry. At East Runton, a man was blown off his bicycle, and fatally injured.

Large areas of King's Lynn were flooded as the Great Ouse, whipped up into a frenzy by the gale, swept over the quay. Thousands of people, without electricity, took refuge in the darkness of their flooded homes and waited hours for the water to recede. The children's ward of the West Norfolk and King's Lynn Hospital was evacuated.

All along the North Norfolk coast waves crashed over the first line of sea defences and families at Hunstanton, Burnham Overy Staithe and Blakeney were forced to flee their homes. Further south at Walcott, householders moved carpets and furniture upstairs as the threat of severe flooding became a reality.

As the wild waters receded, sightseers gathered on the promenade at Hunstanton to see the remains of the old pier.

THE Queen Mother visited St Mary's Church in King's Lynn to look at the damage caused by the 1978 floods, where the tide levels were actually higher than in 1953. On this occasion no-one died but a severe surge funnelled up the Great Ouse and poured over the defences. There was extensive flooding as far inland as Wisbech and the cost of the damage at King's Lynn alone was estimated at £5.5 million. As the Queen Mother was told, the phenomenon of North Sea surge may occur many times a year.

Lasting for only a few hours it is caused by low atmospheric pressure and high winds from the north which whip up a wall of water and drive it southwards. The surge adds about one metre to the tide level but because it usually fails to combine with high water and bad weather there is no flooding risk.

In January 1953, January 1976 and again in January

1978 surges were accompanied by high water and bad weather. It illustrated yet again the importance of maintaining, renewing and replacing the hundreds of miles of coastal defences in the Anglian Region of the National Rivers Authority.

The 1978 surge caused great consternation in London. The water came to within 19 inches of the top of the retaining walls bordering the Thames and the capital's flood control centre became operative. Conditions would have been more grave if the upper reaches of the river had been in flood. For the second time, London was spared a major catastrophe.

Work on a giant flood barrier across the river was underway but it was to be six more years before the great Woolwich project was completed.

The stranded coaster, Function was lifted off the quay at Wells and back into the water.

11th January, 1978 and a wintry sun revealed the night's devastation on Heacham north beach.

Crazy, or brave! This unseasonal dip in the River Yare at Thorpe on 31st December, 1978 by four staff from the Boat and Bottle earned £88 for charity.

1978-9 — a winter of discontent

THE winter of 1978-9 went down in history for the widespread protests over pay and working conditions. As strikers gathered around braziers, with collars upturned to shield them from the icy winds, the weather also staged its own protest. This really was a winter of discontent.

Picket lines at the factory gate were often swept by squalls of snow, tempestuous winds and frosts, so severe, that hot soup brought little relief from the penetrating cold.

As early as the last week of November, 1978 there was a taste of winter with some snow lying in Norfolk. Generally, the weather warmed up in December, even though some cold snaps took hold for a while and ice formed on the River Nene in Peterborough for the first time in 15 years.

After Christmas, temperatures climbed above 50F (10C) and East Anglians were lulled into a false sense of complacency. By the afternoon of 29th December, a sensational blast of cold was heading from Russia where Moscow was suffering its most severe frost for at least 100 years. Most cars in the Russian capital had stopped running as temperatures plunged to -36F (-38C).

Back in eastern England, 30th December dawned cloudy with a north east wind which kept the temperature only a notch above freezing. By the afternoon it was sub zero and the evening saw fiercely cold winds and driving snow, which blew into towering drifts. At Gorleston, waves 15 feet high broke over the pier and stones were thrown up 20 feet on to the promenade. 400 homes at Syderstone, near Fakenham were hit by power cuts.

Ferries bound for Felixstowe were delayed for many hours and a group of 650 Swedish people, due to spend two hours of New Year's Eve at Felixstowe hostelries were forced to abandon their plans and stay at home.

All over Suffolk and Norfolk, roads were blocked. The King's Lynn area was badly hit and snow clearance gangs worked from 5 am each day to clear roads. At Northrepps it was impossible for the postman to get through. On New Year's Day the temperature at RAF Marham, plummeted to 12F (-11C).

There were further falls of snow throughout January and, in February, a vicious spell of wintry weather took hold on the 14th and 15th. The A12 was blocked by drifting snow and a spate of collisions occurred on the Ipswich/Norwich Road just over the border in Essex. A grandfather who had walked waist deep in snow in search of paraffin was found after 19 hours at Belchamp Otten, near Sudbury. He was suffering from exposure but an ambulance got through with the help of a tractor and he survived.

As late as 2nd May, 1979 parts of England suffered winter's sting in the tail. Some hilltops had a light covering of snow on this day.

A small army of volunteers help to dig their way out of Burnham Market on the road to North Creake. This was the scene after the blizzard of February 1979.

CHAPTER ELEVEN: 1980 — 1989

Entertaining and eventful eighties

1980: In May there was a remarkable run of sunny days from 9th to 19th and on 15th and 16th virtually the whole of Britain was clear of cloud, a very rare event. The month only brought 0.2 inches (5mm) of rain to Lowestoft. Norfolk was not quite so lucky on 7th August when, according to one observer, an awesome thunderstorm broke in the Holkham-Wells area. Visibility was reduced to no more than 100 to 200 yards. At Cockthorpe 4.1 inches of rain (105mm) fell and the Fakenham to Creake road became impassable. South of Norwich at Pulham St Mary less than 0.1 inch (2mm) of rain was measured.

1981: While parts of the Midlands and West Country had heavy snow, East Anglia endured 60 hours constant rainfall on 24th - 26th April, producing the worst floods in places since 1947. At Framingham Earl 3.6 inches (92mm) fell in this spell. The Waveney Valley was inundated and around Buxton in the north, farmers were awoken by police on Sunday night as cattle were marooned. Dr Briscoe reported that Buxton was cut off when the road was swept away. On 23rd November, some 105 tornadoes were observed across Britain. At Elmswell, a barn was practically demolished in the village.
A bitterly cold December with the ground snow-covered for over three weeks. The river Wensum was completely frozen over. At Stonham, 400 people spent Sunday night, 13th-14th, in two pubs in the village as the A140 Ipswich to Norwich road became blocked when an eastward moving deep low caused a blizzard. Forty-one passengers were stranded in a coach all night a mile from the village.

1982: Another cold spell in January gave a low of 9F (-13C) at Great Barton. At Stoke-by-Clare in Suffolk, 1.52 inches (39mm) of rain fell in just 25 minutes on 6th June. This is classed as a remarkable fall by hydrologists.

1983: A warm summer. July was the hottest month for England as a whole in a record going back to 1659 with an average maximum as high as 80F (27C) in Suffolk.

1984: Another warm summer but there were some customary thunderstorms and one in the Thetford area severed power supplies to 60,000 consumers. There were reports of 950 lightning strikes. A temperature of 66F (19C) at Bury St Edmunds on the 29th October was the highest recorded in the last week of the month since the station started recording in 1946. Warm southerly winds continued in November with Sahara dust covering car windscreens.

1985: In January and February there were some very cold snowy spells. At Bury St Edmunds the mercury never rose above 23F (-5C) on 16th January, the lowest daytime temperature going back to the start of records in 1946. Heavy drifting snow during 9th - 11th February in the south of Suffolk caused 25 vehicles to be stranded on the Essex-Suffolk border between Sudbury and Colchester at Nayland. Further east even a snowplough became trapped. Yet in the north of Norfolk only 0.03 inches (1mm) of rain fell all month at Potter Heigham.
The storm which had deluged Wimbledon on 5th July developed into a severe hailstorm between Norwich and the north Norfolk coast. There was widespread damage to windows smashed by golfball-sized stones. Many cars had pitted roofs and required a complete respray. At Coltishall a squall gusted to 78mph. Crops were devastated with sugar-beet leaves shredded and cereals flattened. At Dilham, six inches of hail still blocked the fronts of garages the next day and had to be shovelled away. It was estimated that the agricultural loss amounted to £1,000,000. However, the temperature did reach an outstanding 82F (28C) at Bury St Edmunds on 1st October.

1986: In many parts of Norfolk and Suffolk temperatures did not rise above 39F (4C) throughout February, the second coldest behind 1947 this century and to complete the arctic-like feel to the month, the aurora flickered in the chill night sky on 9th and 20th. Winds gusted to 75mph in the Norwich area on 24th March. Power lines were brought down as the pressure dropped to 28.70 inches (972 millibars) at Beccles. Aldeburgh was blacked out twice by trees falling onto cables.

1987: A year made memorable by several weather events including the snows of January and the Great Storm of October 15th-16th. Drifting reached 10 feet in height near Lowestoft with only 49 out of Suffolk's 380 schools remaining open. Birds were washed ashore encased in ice at Bacton as temperatures failed to reach 19F (-7C) on 12th January.

1988: After a wet January with rain on 29 days at Lowestoft and a total of 6.17 inches at Aldeburgh, the sunshine recorder worked overtime at Wattisham in February with a record 127 hours measured. Many places failed to record a single air frost in December but this did not stop a 'flu epidemic sweeping Britain.

1989: At Ipswich, January and February were the warmest since 1921. A record breaking low pressure system moved across England on 25th February and sent the glass down to around 28.10 inches (952 millibars), the lowest value since Christmas 1821. It was one of the warmest, sunniest and driest Mays of the century with more than 300 hours of sunshine at Beccles and other places.

There were very icy conditions on the roads between 10th and 12th January, 1981, resulting in numerous accidents. At Newmarket, the stable lads, exercising the horses, took special care.

A blizzard swept across East Anglia during the night of Sunday 13th December, 1981. It was particularly bad in west Suffolk where hundreds of cars, buses, lorries and even ambulances, were abandoned. Picture shows the scene at Fordham Road, Isleham, near Newmarket.

There was snow on the ground in many places during the Christmas holiday, 1981 and towards the end of the month a rapid thaw set in, bringing with it the inevitable flooding. The Newmarket area again suffered badly. This is Moulton where the River Kennett was swollen with floodwater and broken ice.

The blizzards returned in the New Year to the delight of many children. This was the scene on the pond at Boughton, near Downham Market on 15th January, 1982.

ABOVE: As far as is known, the Great Ouse at King's Lynn has never completely frozen over although "the cut" from the river which runs through Wiggenhall has been totally frozen on a few occasions. This picture shows pancake ice floes at Lynn South Quay in January 1982. The Lynn swans had a hard time.

The snow in January, 1982 reduced many roads to a single track in places, including the A12 between Colchester and Ipswich. As the temperatures plummeted, the sea froze and boats were held fast on the ice. It was on 10th January, 1982 that Britain experienced the lowest-recorded temperature of all time — -17F (-27C) at Braemar, Scotland. Picture shows how water dripping off branches at Great Snoring froze into dazzling, clinking icicles on this record breaking day.

Too much water, then suddenly too little. The exceptional dry weather in the autumn of 1985 led to the river at Exning, a tributary of the Cam, drying up. This was the picture on 16th November.

The great blizzard of 1987

IN spite of reports that the greenhouse effect may have warmed up the planet, the coldest day ever known in East Anglia occurred during the savage wintry weather which crippled Norfolk and Suffolk in January 1987. Snow, whipped up into drifts more than 15 feet, isolated rural villages and many major roads were blocked for almost a week.

The bitter weather arrived from Russia and Scandinavia on Saturday 10th January when temperatures in Helsinki, the Finnish capital, plummeted to a record-breaking -36F (-38C).

This exceptionally cold air began to flow westwards towards Eastern England. Although the sea had warmed the air, saving Britain from these Continental extremes, it led to the formation of towering clouds which shed millions of tons of snow as they drifted over Suffolk, Norfolk, Essex, Kent and Surrey.

By the afternoon of 10th January the temperature was at or below freezing point and, in fact, the maximum at Lowestoft was only 27F. The snow showers set in and continued for the next few days, becoming heavier as the week progressed. Monday 12th January saw remarkably low maximum temperatures. Many places in Suffolk failed to see the mercury climb above 18F (-8C), a figure so low that nothing in the record books this century could compare with it. At Belstead Hall, Suffolk, the top temperature was 21F(-6C), the lowest lunchtime reading this century. That night, Marham in Norfolk, suffered 27 degrees of frost (-15C).

By Tuesday 13th January, further snow fell and the next day it was drifting heavily in strong north easterly winds which touched 45mph on the coast. Undrifted snow lay to a depth of 14 inches at RAF Coltishall, Norfolk. The thousands of tons of fine, powdery snow blew into giant drifts which isolated villages for days and blocked hundreds of roads, including the A47 between Norwich and Yarmouth and the A12 at Saxmundham.

There were some dramatic moments in the snowbound villages. Helicopters were called in to rescue people needing hospital treatment. One landed at Barney near Fakenham when a mum-to-be rang to say she was in labour. Similar SOS calls came from Cawston and Watton. The women were flown to Hewett School playing fields and were then taken by ambulance along the icy roads to the Norfolk and Norwich Hospital. A JCB had been called to clear a path to the house at Barney for the ambulance but, as soon as the snow had been shovelled aside, it blew back with great fury, filling in the passage within minutes. Another mercy mission was undertaken at North Walsham where a seriously ill man was airlifted to Norwich.

There were problems in the hospitals themselves. Thirty patients escaped the threat of evacuation when vital supplies of oil only just got through to Mundersley Hospital in time.

As many as 80 schools in Suffolk closed and offices remained empty or sparsely occupied. In the shops there was panic buying, for weathermen were unable to predict when the great freeze would end. Bread was rationed to two loaves per person at several stores, including the Gateway branches at Dereham. At Colkirk a pensioner died from his exertions while shovelling snow from around his home. At Old Buckenham near Attleborough, a snow clearing JCB caught fire. The flames were extinguished by the driver of another JCB shovelling snow onto the blazing vehicle.

The heavy snow destroyed large areas of reedbeds on the Broads and material for thatching was in short supply. Nature lovers said birds such as kingfishers and bitterns were thought to have perished in the abnormally icy conditions. At Ipswich the town hall clock stopped. The long hand had become stuck in snow. British Telecom said that so many people were making phone calls to check on friends and family that the service was beginning to crack.

Police in Suffolk warned drivers not to take their cars out unless their journeys were absolutely essential but, in West Suffolk the roads were in a much better condition than near the coast, which suffered the heaviest falls. There were ice skating competitions on the Fens and a West Norfolk farmer, Melton Morris, took on Olympic skater John French and lost. There was some disappointment at Downham Market when would-be skaters found that boats had cracked the ice on the Well Creek. They felt that as the water so seldom froze it was appropriate to ask boat owners not to try to navigate the creek.

So few jurors turned up at Norwich Crown Court that trials were postponed and the courts closed for three days. Norwich airport was snowbound. No flights took off or landed at the height of the cold snap. At Wangford and Kessingland a doctor and his wife borrowed a tractor to reach their surgeries and patients. It took workmen three days to cut a passage through the snow so that Lound and St Olaves, near Great Yarmouth, could once again be linked by road.

At sea, conditions were atrocious. The crew of a Lowestoft fishing vessel reported the worst conditions ever known in the North Sea with a force 10 gale near the Danish coast and severe wind chill. The skippers reported that it would take 12 hours to free the winches of ice so that fishing could resume.

After several more days of grey skies, severe frost and light snow showers, a gradual thaw with thick fog replaced the record-breaking cold weather. Very slowly, the two counties melted and, by the end of the month, life had slowly reverted to normal.

The thick icebergs may have given an arctic touch to the waterfront at King's Lynn but they also posed quite a problem for the ferryman, Reg Hare and his assistant Keith Brown who is seen here contemplating how to negotiate the ferry through the obstacle course. During this extraordinary spell of cold weather, the bergs in the Great Ouse rose 12 feet from the river bed and could withstand the weight of a man. Mr Hare said at the time: "We had a few like this in 1963 but this is the worst I have known".

Half way across — the West Lynn ferry boat refuses to be beaten.

The icy waters of the Waveney at Beccles, framed by the iron girders of the road bridge.

Norwich in the Ice Age!   This was the Wensum on 14th January, 1987.

Taking the dogs for a walk in Bramford Lane, Ipswich on 12th January, 1987 — one of the coldest days of the century — was an exhilarating experience.

The cows are not yet lying down but as the storm clouds gather over St Faiths, near Norwich, it seems that a massive deluge is imminent.

It was a storm of a different kind that made the headlines on Saturday 22nd August, 1987 when a line of cumulo-nimbus clouds, some reaching seven miles high developed to the south-west of Ipswich. The storm struck with great intensity. It became dark as night and massive hail devastated the Woodbridge area. Windows were smashed, car roofs and bonnets pitted. At one nursery in Ufford, £100,000 of damage was done in minutes. Golf ball hail flattened gardens, tearing to shreds plants and flowers. The equivalent of a month's rain fell in just 45 minutes, causing a landslide at Brantham, closing the railway line to London. Hundreds of people fled from their flooded homes and dozens of roads were blocked by abandoned vehicles. Then came the Great October Storm, felling in just an hour or so a million trees leaving whole forests no more than acres of tattered stumps.

Chad Brook was in full flood at Long Melford on 12th October, swamping bungalows at Old Court.

Floodwaters reach crisis level

10th October, 1987

WITH blizzards in January, storms in March and a July deluge of unusual violence, 1987 was proving to be a turbulent year. Now, in this wet October, there were floods all over East Anglia. In Suffolk, the Deben burst its banks, swamping the surrounding land. So did the Orwell, the Waveney and the Gipping. But it was the Stour which caused the greatest concern, the river reaching its highest level for 20 years in the Sudbury area, after unprecedented torrents of rain.

As emergency services went on full alert, police helped householders move furniture upstairs and livestock was taken to higher ground. Homes at Long Melford were badly flooded and firemen pumped water from downstairs rooms. At Park Corner, an emergency dam was built and, at Sudbury, firemen launched the brigade dinghy and rescued two children who were marooned in meadows near the town's Mill Hotel.

At Sudbury, almost 3 inches of rain had fallen in seven days. It was the same story in the Gipping Valley. Hundreds of sandbags were handed out to residents in Stowmarket, Needham Market, Bramford and Stratford St Andrew by Mid-Suffolk Council's emergency team. On the Suffolk-Essex border at Stratford St Mary, police called on householders and advised them to move as a torrent of water made conditions "highly dangerous".

Suffolk Police's Martlesham HQ received 295 reports of flooding. Houses at Witnesham, Framlingham, Kesgrave and Cavendish were badly hit. At Leiston, a police car became marooned by floodwater and, on the A45 at Haughley, a car overturned as the driver hit a wall of floodwater.

By Monday 12th October, the floods were, for a time, past their peak but flood defences in Ipswich were still in operation to control the flow of water into the Orwell Basin. As the floods subsided, people wondered, could Mother Nature possibly throw anything else at East Anglia?

The answer came in the early hours of Friday 16th October, 1987...

The greatest storm in history?

16th October, 1987

THIS was a night that no-one at the time living in southern or eastern England will ever forget. It began with empty milk bottles cartwheeling down the road and dustbin lids rattling furiously. It ended with a storm of such unbelievable violence that homes were devastated, trees ripped up by the million, cars crushed and communications crippled. In a few hours of wild fury the face of the landscape was changed for ever.

The storm, driven on by hurricane-force winds, hit Suffolk and Norfolk in the small hours but, as dawn approached, the wind increased in speed and violence. It grabbed everything in its path, shaking, twisting, tossing and felling. Caravan parks were reduced to matchwood. Houses, schools, hospitals and hotels had roofs lifted off. Greenhouses were destroyed. Boats were tossed ashore. Electricity pylons tumbled like skittles, sending high-voltage cables writhing and arcing through the night like lightning. Ancient trees were toppled and in the great Suffolk forests, hundreds of thousands of conifers were upturned or beheaded.

When the people of East Anglia dared to look, they found their homes and gardens battered, the landscape rearranged and, in many harrowing cases, their premises or possessions flattened. History had been proclaimed by the roar of the wind; there was madness abroad that mid-October morning and a stunned population could do nothing about it.

There had been nothing unusual about the weather forecast. Storm winds were reported to be sweeping across the Atlantic, but they were going to miss Britain. Just after midnight, trees began to go down on the Channel Islands. At 2.30 am, a man was killed in Sussex when a chimney pot toppled into his bedroom. An hour later high voltage power lines in Kent were "tripping" as the National Grid began to fail. By 4.50 am, weather observation stations in Essex were measuring wind speeds of 87 knots, exactly 100 mph. Suffolk and Norfolk were next in line.

Suffolk's magnificent churches, with few hills of any size to protect them from the wind, faced the full fury of the onslaught. Cransford Baptist Church was demolished and so was Trimley Methodist. The roof was ripped off the Catholic Church in Leiston. Three trees fell onto the parish church of Thelnetham and one giant cedar tree onto Westhall near Halesworth. Ditchingham lost a pinnacle on top of its tower, St Edmunds at Southwold, a flagstaff and weathervane. St Mary's Church, Uggeshall and St Mary's Church, Newbourne each lost an east wall and a stained glass window.

The city of Ipswich, more sheltered than open country, still suffered badly. Huge aluminium girders were stripped off the Ipswich bus garage and wrapped round a row of double deckers, the social centre at St Clement's Hospital lost two walls and, in the Ipswich parks, many years of carefully nurtured landscape was transformed into a tangled wreckage. So great was the destruction that the parks were closed to the public while tree surgeons and arborists worked long hours to remove dangerous branches and take away the carcasses of fallen oaks.

Lorry drivers, unfortunate to be on the road, came to grief on the Orwell Bridge, aeroplanes on the ground were upturned, boats on the Broads were ripped from their moorings and drifted helplessly down swollen rivers. All along the coast there was vast damage. Scores of beachhuts disintegrated, cafes and amusement arcades lost their windows and chimneys crashed through roofs. In North Suffolk every road was blocked by fallen trees and every village cut off from its neighbour. The East Anglian rail network was paralysed and only the Norwich to Lowestoft service managed to operate.

If the sturdy buildings of Ipswich were vulnerable, then the mature Scots and Corsican pines in the Rendlesham, Tunstall and Dunwich forests stood no chance. The trees were either snapped off below the half way mark or entire root systems were lifted from the ground; it was as if a giant had toured the forests with a scythe. Experts estimated that in the three big forests, one million trees had been toppled or, put another way, there was 13 years' wood supply in various horizontal angles. Somehow it had to be extracted. It had taken 60 years for the saplings, planted in the early 1920's, to grow into great tall forests. On that unforgettable morning it took the wind 60 minutes to destroy them.

No-one in Suffolk died as a result of the storm but there were many miraculous escapes. Megan McSloy, aged 10 months, of Melford Road, Stowmarket was asleep in her bedroom when an enormous oak tree crashed through the roof of her house, coming to rest less than 15 feet from where she lay. It demolished a garage and damaged three houses but Megan was unhurt. Tracey Sharman, aged 19 of Milden Road, Ipswich was even luckier. Awoken by the wind, she decided to go into her mother's bedroom. As she left a tree came through the roof of her bedroom and landed on the bed. She would have been badly hurt. June Laplace, of Rendelsham Road, Ipswich owes her life to her son. During the night, the roof of her bedroom fell in and she was trapped under a pile of bricks and choking dust and rubble. Her son managed to pull her out of bed and onto the landing as the rest of the bedroom roof fell in.

At Felixstowe, a massive gust tore a 1,300 ton tanker away from its mooring and then hurled it

The remains of the Baptist Church at Cransford, Suffolk, seen from the pulpit.

against the side of the jetty. On board the *Silverfalcon* were 13 officers who realised they were sitting on a "time bomb", for the ship was loaded with industrial chemicals. If they were to explode it would be the end of the *Silverfalcon*, the men and most of Felixstowe Port. As drifting or sinking barges were being torpedoed into the ship and sparks were flying, the decision was made to close the Port and evacuate people from their nearby homes. A salvage team then boarded the listing ship and, with a nitrogen "blanket", made the deadly cargo safe.

There were moments of great drama in Norfolk, too. Forty platform workers had to be airlifted from a gas rig off Cromer as a stricken vessel drifted dangerously close. Lifeboatmen braved the most appalling seas to go to the aid of a British coaster off Yarmouth, where coastguards reported force 11 winds.

As with Suffolk, fallen trees blocked many roads and the damage in the National Trust gardens of Blickling, Felbrigg and Sheringham was appalling. Thetford Forest also suffered and it was estimated that 20,000 cubic metres were completely "wiped out". Sadly, there was one fatality in the county. Farmer, Sidney Riches died in his wrecked car at Tottenhill after colliding with a lorry at a point where the A10 was blocked by fallen trees.

Right across East Anglia, miles and miles of overhead power cables were brought down, either by the wind or falling trees. Transformers were wrenched from the ground, poles snapped like twigs and lights went out. Eastern Electricity said at the time that they had never experienced such devastation in their history. In this unprecedented situation, one in four of the Board's 2.8 million customers were affected.

Helicopters were brought in to survey the lines and locate faults. Extra engineers and linesmen were drafted in from all over England. The army sent men with special lifting gear to even the most remote corners of Norfolk and Suffolk. Emergency generators were delivered to convalescent centres, nursing homes and meat stores, and help lines were established at EEB offices giving advice on how to cope with the emergency.

One of the the most dramatic stories concerned the fate of Jomo, a spotted leopard at Thrigby Hall Wildlife Gardens whose cage was fixed to a tree that looked in danger of toppling in the wind. Director, Mrs Beryl Sims, worried that Jomo might escape into the Norfolk countryside, called a vet who considered firing a tranquillising dart. Discovering the dart would not hit its target in a force 10 wind, the vet called the police and three marksmen arrived from Norwich. With their sights fixed on the leopard, they waited for the tree to fall. The tree survived...and so did Jomo.

Across southern and eastern England there had been nothing to compare with the cost of the 1987 storm, or "hurricane" as many newspapers described it. As claims from private businessmen and householders began to flood in, the full enormity of that single night of fury began to emerge. The Association of British Insurers estimated that the final compensation bill was in excess of £1.5 billion pounds. It was the biggest ever payout caused by the weather — a catastrophic meteorological event that, according to the law of averages, was unlikely to happen for another 250 years.

Little more than two years later, on 25th January, 1990....Norfolk and Suffolk were reeling again.

Rendlesham Forest, one of the last strongholds for the red squirrel, lost an estimated 400, 000 trees in the early hours of 16th October, 1987.

The massive roots of an old oak, with jaws wide open, provide a wonderful new place to play for Stewart Buttle, seen here with his grandmother, Eliza. The photograph was taken in the grounds of Thornham Magna Estate by Roy Buttle, landlord of The Bull at Yaxley, near Eye, Suffolk, close to the Norfolk border. Roy and his wife Margaret will never forget THAT night when the wind roared and the pub moved on its foundations. "We thought the old Bull was about to charge", said Margaret. Another person who will never forget is the bed-and-breakfast guest in the garden caravan who thought the world was coming to an end. His nearly did!

Jomo the spotted leopard from Thrigby Hall Wildlife Park who survived the storm — and the police marksmen!

The Waxham Great Barn, a valuable sixteenth century thatched building, near Winterton, Norfolk, which was virtually destroyed by the wind. Thanks to English Heritage and Norfolk County Council it was restored at a cost of £430,000, the work being completed in July, 1993.

A twister, as pictured here, is another way of describing a tornado, and an apt one, because the air rotates or twists very rapidly within the funnel, creating low pressure in the centre. This photograph of a Norfolk twister was taken by Mrs Cynthia Gibling of Chedgrave on 13th April, 1989 to the south-west of Loddon.

Mrs Gibling saw a terrific line in the sky, bright and clear to one side and very black on the other. The funnel cloud was on the edge of it.

There was another tornado on 14th December. This one swept through the Suffolk village of Long Stratton, destroyed a shop and damaged 100 houses. According to one report, a man looked out of the Angel Public House in time to see his car pass by upside down with the windows being plucked out. Another man, sitting in the pub car park, suddenly heard a bang in the sky and spotted a metal barrel flying straight at the car. He reclined his seat just in time before it smashed through the driver's door window and shot out of the other side of the car. The heart of the village looked as if a bomb had exploded. It was caused by an area of low pressure setting off thunderstorms along a marked temperature boundary between warm air to the south and cold air over northern England. One storm was accompanied by the tornado. It is estimated that winds may have reached 130 mph.

CHAPTER TWELVE: 1990—1993

The great drought continued

1990: In another Great Storm, 47 people died across Britain on the 25th January, including a man in Swaffham crushed by a tree, as an intense low pressure system moved east across Scotland. Nationally, three million trees were blown down. At Landguard Point, Suffolk, a gust of 90 mph was measured.

There was compensation a few weeks later with the warmest March for 60 years and a very warm, dry summer with temperatures reaching 93F (34C) in many places on 3rd August. The year was even sunnier than 1989 with 1,948 hours at Beccles. The coldest night of the year was actually recorded in April with a low of 24F (-4.5C) on the 5th. At Gressenhall, Norfolk, a snow shower on 8th December gave nearly three inches of snow in 30 minutes, yet two miles down the road there was no snow at all.

1991: The year was even drier than 1976 and was the driest since 1972 at Lowestoft. Just 15.3 inches (391mm) of rain fell. It was also famous for the "wrong sort of snow" when commuters to London in February were held up by some loose, powdery snow which penetrated automatic door mechanisms, rendering them inoperable. Frost on up to eight days in April was quite sharp at night around the 20th and early potatoes were badly affected.

1992: Another year in which drought stole the headlines. At Washpit Farm, Borehole, near King's Lynn a combination of low rainfall, high evaporation losses and dry soils meant that winter replenishment of ground water was only half that recorded for any previous four-year sequence in a 40 year record. There is no close precedent this century.

1993: A combination of north-west gales and very high spring-tides on 21st February led to widespread damage along the coast in an otherwise settled month. Waves reached 20 feet in height with Lowestoft taking a pounding. The harbour bridge was put out of action for three days by sea water inundating hydraulic and electrical systems and badly disrupting shipping. Sea defences were breached in both counties. Marham had five inches of snow in March.

The highs and lows of East Anglia

HIGHEST TEMPERATURE		LOWEST TEMPERATURE		DRIEST YEAR	
NORFOLK	SUFFOLK	NORFOLK	SUFFOLK	NORFOLK	SUFFOLK
97.1F (36.2C) at Hillington on 9th August, 1911	95F (35C) at Flixton on 19th August, 1932	-1.5F (-18.9C) at Santon Downham on 23rd January, 1963	-1F (-18.3C) at Thurlow on 10th February, 1895	1921 with only 10.5 inches (268mm) of rain at Outwell	1921 with only 11.21 inches (286 mm) at Bradfield St George

WETTEST DAY		WETTEST YEARS	SUNNIEST YEAR	SNOWIEST YEAR
NORFOLK	SUFFOLK			
7.31 inches (186mm) at Brundall on 26th August, 1912	5 inches (127mm) at Stradbroke on 26th August, 1912	1912 with 40.74 inches (1040mm) of rain at Norwich and 1872 with 1020 mm in the East Dereham area	1911 with 2,000 hours of sun in places and 1,945 hours at Ipswich	1963 when snow lay on the ground for 64 days at Santon Downham

The strongest wind recorded was 108 mph at Cromer on 2nd-3rd January, 1976

Another killer storm hits Anglia

25th January, 1990

IT seemed quite inconceivable that after the October 1987 "hurricane" another great storm could strike within three years. On 25th January, 1990, with ample warnings from the Met. Office, a deep area of low pressure crossed the country, producing howling winds which screamed at hurricane force across East Anglia.

Nationally, 47 people died, compared to 19 in the '87 tempest, but this time the storm affected a larger area of England at a busier time of the day. Once again, thousands of homes were blacked out as overhead power lines came down. Hundreds of roads were blocked by fallen trees and many homes lost tiles or suffered more extensive damage. Trains were brought to a standstill and ferries halted. Country-wide, about four million trees fell compared with 15 million in 1987.

Two men were killed when a pine tree crashed on to a car on the Norwich to Watton Road at Scoulton. At March, a railway worker was killed when he was blown off his bike. In Norwich, two women were hurt when a hoarding fell from a building in London Street.

A member of Dereham Council surveyor's department experienced the effects of the storm first hand when he was struck on the head by a flying slate. The raging winds blew off the roof of a portable building in Yarmouth, injuring a workman. A lorry driver was injured when his vehicle was blown into a dyke at Acle Straight.

Norwich Airport stood four square in the path of the gale. Cars had to be parked in front of aircraft to prevent them from blowing away and many incoming flights were diverted to other airports. The wind reached a mean speed of 60 mph in Norfolk with gusts registering in excess of 70 mph. At Felixstowe, a gust of 80 mph was recorded but it is likely that much higher speeds were attained where anemometers were not located.

Around 150 passengers spent 10 tortured hours in the Sealink UK flagship St Nicholas. They eventually reached the Hook of Holland late the following day. A tractor driver was killed by a falling tree near Newmarket. A few miles away, at Mildenhall, a man was trapped in his van which had crashed into a wall after being struck by falling branches. Another motorist was trapped on the A134 at Sicklesmere. A tree hit the back of his car and he careered into a field. In Ashley, an elderly couple managed to scramble free from their wrecked car which was also struck by a tree.

At Wangford, a barn collapsed onto a fish and chip shop and at Cromer, three men fled from the pier seconds before the amusement arcade was demolished. There was a similar incident at Felixstowe where a helter skelter was blown over.

Commuters at Norwich station waited for more than five hours to catch a train to London. Some spent the night in the city's hotels.

At Sheringham, a large section of roof was blown off the ex-servicemen's club and came down on a car. A woman was trapped for three hours when the roof caved in at her top-storey flat in Yarmouth. At Newbourne, near Ipswich, an angel crashed through the roof of the chapel of St Mary's where builders had just completed restoration work after the damage caused in 1987.

Following the gale, many people were injured trying to clear fallen trees. An agricultural worker at Stradishall, a motorist at Blythburgh and a resident of Leiston were some of the victims.

It was generally accepted that the 1990 storm was one of the worst of the century. Nationally, insurance companies put the bill at £2,000 million — a similar figure to that of 1987.

A remarkable picture of a lorry on Beccles by-pass in some considerable danger during the January gale of 1990.

Wrecked roof tiles at Norwich. Many areas of the city suffered similar damage.

The amusement arcade at Cromer Pier was smashed to pieces — an incident which may not have displeased all local people!

At the Charles Mannings Amusements at Felixstowe, the helter skelter went helter skelter.

Worst drought of the century

1988 — 1992

AS rain poured down from leaden skies in January, 1988, one of the wettest months of the century, with 28 days of rain at Lowestoft, who would have thought that drought would be a major talking point in the months ahead ?

Cracked river beds, hosepipe restrictions and vanishing wildlife were to replace flooded fields and waterlogged gardens. The perils of swirling waters were exchanged for the menace of subsidence as clay soils dried out.

The process had already begun by 18th April when Bury St Edmunds basked in temperatures of 74F (23C). It continued in the summer when Old Costessey, Norfolk had its driest June since 1977 and it was the same story in the winter when Norwich had its driest December since 1933. But it was in the year 1989 that the weather made people think that East Anglia had slipped southwards towards the Mediterranean.

Between 1st May and 31st August parts of Suffolk boasted a record 1,000 hours' sunshine. In May alone there were 331 hours of sun at Wattisham, figures that could do justice to the Costa del Sol. Even more surprising was that November, normally a gloomy month, had only 0.4 inches (10mm) of rain at Aldeburgh and there were 112 hours of sunshine at Higham. During this spectacular month the sun failed to shine on just one day at East Dereham.

By 1990, worries began to grow about dwindling water supplies. With mainly southwest winds in January and February, East Anglia was relatively dry compared to the west of Britain where torrents of rain fell. It was little wonder that during a March that saw only 0.27 inches (7mm) at Levington and 0.35 inches (8.9mm) at Rushmere St Andrew, dust storms should cover roads several inches deep in soil at Martlesham.

Ipswich enjoyed a sunny 70F (21C) on 18th March, a forerunner to one of the sunniest springs of the century. Between 28th April and 6th May, the sun shone from brilliant blue skies and the temperature actually touched 80F (27C) in Ipswich.

July brought an intensification of both heat and drought. The mercury soared to 89F (32C) at Framingham Earl in Norfolk on the 20th and only 0.35 inch (8.9mm) fell all month at Landguard Point. The high temperature and bountiful sunshine was thought responsible for the breeding rate of rabbits. Their prolific numbers ate through £120 million worth of crops in East Anglia and led to farmers putting birth control pills into rabbit holes!

There were other phenomena. A tortoise in Wells laid an egg for the first time in 28 years and the city of Norwich and its environs was beset by a plague of wasps. The environmental health department dealt with more than 500 nests by the end of July — not normally their busy time.

Conditions were ripe for even hotter weather. A static anticyclone lay to the east of Britain wafting up hot Continental air and a dry ground prevented the sun wasting its energy by evaporating surface moisture. The mercury responded. On Friday 3rd August, many long-term records were broken with 99F (37.2C) at Cheltenham, a new British record high. In Norfolk, Pulham St Mary reached 93.6F (34.6C), not quite a county record. A Norwich based skin specialist advised people to "slip, slop and slap" — slip on a T-shirt, slop on sun cream and slap on a hat — catchy advice, well-known in Australia.

Throughout East Anglia, shorts became the order of the day and shop staff wore attire more akin to the tropics. For Ronaldo's, the ice cream manufacturer, it was the busiest period in the company's history and the staff worked round the clock to satiate the public's desire.

Staff at an Ipswich bakery became really hot under the collar. Thirty employees of Tooks walked out when the internal temperature reached 100F (38C). There was also a big demand for deodorant and sales nationwide in August amounted to £500,000.

In the country the searing heat caused many problems and both Norfolk and Suffolk Fire Brigades were at full stretch. In July, Norfolk received 1,250 calls; double the average, and a campaign was launched to "stop the county burning". Thousands of leaflets were distributed to warn of the hazards of the tinder dry countryside. A 100-acre field of crops went up in flames at Palgrave, near Diss. In West Suffolk, firecrews had a more unusual job. As well as dealing with grass and stubble fires they had to douse chicken huts with water to cool them down and so prevent the chickens roasting!

Commuters had many delayed journeys as fires raged, particularly alongside the Norwich to London line. Limits of 20 mph below top speed were also imposed because of the possibility that lines would buckle in the heat.

By October, a legacy of the long dry summer, far worse than withered lawns and stunted vegetables, was that of cracked and distorted walls, warped windows and door frames. The problem was subsidence as clay soils dried out and shrank. One engineering firm in Hadleigh handled eight cases a week in the autumn, twice their normal figure.

The winter of 1990-1 continued to be dry with Lowestoft recording only 65 per cent of its average rainfall and, the following spring, only 45 per cent of average. The summer of 1991, in spite of a wet June,

A dried-up pond at Syderstone, Norfolk — in 1991 home to the rare Natterjack toad.

was also drier than average and water diviner, Herbert Chappell from Little Walsingham was kept busy looking for old wells as gardens dried up and lawns, still denied the use of sprinklers, yellowed and withered.

One ghostly aspect of the dry conditions were the glimpses of the past that were revealed. Air reconnaissance showed markings on ripening crops under stress in drought conditions. Discoveries such as a Romano-Celtic Temple at Pentney and a Roman Temple at Caistor St Edmund were among the host of ancient finds revealed as brightly coloured marks in fields. At Walsingham, populated now entirely by sheep, the earthwork remains of streets and house plots of Egmere, a deserted medieval village, were seen with startling clarity.

Drought is insidious, a creeping menace built up from a long run of drier than average conditions. After a winter that gave only 56 per cent of long-term rainfall, East Anglia had, by the spring of 1992, built up a total deficit of 20 inches in four years. The Ministry of Agriculture devised an amber and red warning system for farmers to warn them in advance of impending irrigation restrictions.

By 25th May, when temperatures reached 82F (28C), water companies across the east and south of Britain said they "were into unchartered waters" for underground supplies had never been so low. It was the worst drought since the 1740's.

Nature, of course, relented. August, 1992 brought welcome rain, with winds up to 50 mph. In September, thunderstorms hit Suffolk and floodwaters and mudslides blocked roads in Hadleigh and Ipswich. Two thousand homes in Bury St Edmunds, Stowmarket and Sudbury were blacked out as lightning hit power cables. 1.29 inches (33mm) fell at East Dereham and cars were reported to be floating in floodwaters at Sudbury.

Gradually, the word "drought" left the headlines and rain fell steadily during the autumn and early winter. In October 1992 it was officially declared to be over.

Mother Nature did provide one reminder, however. February 1993 was the driest in Suffolk since 1959 and March had only four days of rain.

Hunstanton beach, during August 1990 — when the temperature climbed, and stayed, in the nineties for several days.

Green algae was fouling the propellers of small craft on the barren River Lark, near Bury St Edmunds during the August drought of 1990. Photograph shows Peter Bangs and, in the background, the reed infested river, which was in danger of turning stagnant. At Needham Market, watersports on the Needham lake were banned as toxic algae threatened. At the Farnham Park Golf Course in Bury, the lakes evaporated and trains between London and Norwich were delayed because overhead power cables were sagging in the heat. Some businesses suffered but others did well. The staff of Atco lawmowers were put on a three-day week while the brewers, Greene King sold record supplies of beer. There was a freak act of nature in Mount Road, Bury when straw from a harvested field swirled up to create amazing spheres the size of houses. According to an eye-witness, it was eerie, but beautiful. Photograph below shows an Alpaca at Kilverston Park enjoying a cool period on the hottest day of the century, 2nd August, 1990.

Now there is no defence against would-be assailants. This is the moat surrounding Baconsthorpe Castle, near Holt as the great drought takes its toll.

The scene of devastation left by the tornado at Dullingham.

Tornado brings terror to a village

13th November, 1991

A TORNADO lasting about four minutes ripped through the village of Dullingham, near the Suffolk/Cambridge border on Wednesday 13th November, 1991. A barn filled with thousands of pounds worth of vintage vehicles was wrecked as falling trees brought power lines down. About 20 homes were without electricity for several hours.

The tornado ploughed a 2,000-yard strip through the village. Buildings less than 100 feet from its path remained unscathed and no-one was injured. Albert Spurling, whose bungalow roof was lifted off said it was the most frightening experience of his life. All his lounge windows were smashed, the fence came down and his car was badly damaged.

The landlord of The Boot pub which also lost its roof said the tornado struck at 7.30 as he was serving customers. He said there was an almighty roar, followed by torrential rain then a noise like an express train hitting the buffers.

This was the second time in 13 years that the area around Newmarket had been hit by a tornado, which is formed by the rapid displacement of warm moist air by cold dense air, often in association with violent thunderstorms along a cold front. Tornadoes are not all that rare, but those caught in the path of one are very unlucky.

February, 1991 brought freezing temperatures and almost 11 inches of snow to a shivering East Anglia. Many schools were closed and pavements were so snowbound that pedestrians walked in the road, prompting Suffolk police to make a special plea, advising walkers to face oncoming traffic. Many services to Liverpool Street also failed to run, British Rail blaming the powdery variety of snow for clogging up engines. "It was the wrong type", they announced. Picture shows snow lovers on the winter slopes of Christchurch Park, Ipswich.

Damaged by lightning

IT WAS early morning on 18th September, 1992 when lightning struck several buildings in Norwich, including the cathedral, which escaped serious damage. Of greater concern was the damage to sensitive electronic equipment such as computers, fax machines and photocopiers which were put out of action.

Boys from Norwich School were waiting to enter the Cathedral for morning assembly when there was a flash, an explosion and alarm bells started to ring. Thousands of homes were without power in Wymondham, Swaffham, Watton and Wells. The Eastern Electricity radio mast at Chedburgh was also struck, destroying vital commuications.

Many houses were evacuated after being hit by lightning in the villages of Great Livermere, Cavendish, Laxfield, Brockley and Wroxham, where a bedroom was entirely wrecked. Photograph shows June Matthewson and her son Oliver inspecting the damage.

SEAL TRIPS
BLAKENEY POINT
TICKETS
HERE

The tide swept in too quickly for the owner of this Volvo. He abandoned the vehicle at Blakeney Quay and made a dash for safety as the sea took control.

Bungalows washed away at Walcott

21st February, 1993

IT HAD been 15 years since the last time a North Sea surge had joined with the lethal combination of strong north-westerly winds and high tides so perhaps this one was well overdue. On 21st February, 1993 this conjunction of the elements brought flooding, alerts and evacuations right down the east coast.

Three holiday bungalows were washed away and 120 people evacuated at Walcott. A caravan site and a number of houses near Cley were flooded and five bungalows collapsed at Hemsby when their foundations were washed away. The defences were breached at Salthouse and Weybourne.

Low-lying buildings in the Reedham Ferry area were flooded when the River Yare burst its banks and the A143 was closed near Haddiscoe. More than 400 people were evacuated from their homes at Gorleston after a flood alert in the Great Yarmouth area and a section of the A47 was closed when a break opened up in the bank of the River Bure.

In Suffolk, a cafe and several beach huts were destroyed in Southwold and homes were flooded at Aldeburgh. A vast lake formed around Walberswick and sea defences were breached in many places.

Among those evacuated was a seven-month old baby and her parents who were staying in the yacht club near the water's edge.

All round the coastal communities of Norfolk and Suffolk, emergency services were put on standby and flood alerts broadcast on radio and television. Evacuation centres were prepared and flood prevention procedures activated with scores of gates in sea defences closed against the waves. As the region went to the brink of a flood disaster, the billion pounds worth of defences paid off, and a second high tide passed without major incident.

The emergency caused a big debate over new multi-million pound defence schemes for the Broads. National Rivers Authority engineer, Mike Childs told the *Eastern Daily Press* that the North Sea was forecast to rise two feet in the next century and the price of complacency was likely to be high. "We cannot afford to let them decline."

In the North Sea, nearer to the Dutch coast, a Swedish grain carrier capsized and sank after the crew had been winched to safety.

An even bigger tide a few weeks later was, fortunately, greeted by calm conditions. Nature can be kind!

Beach chalets perch precariously on the edge of the cliffs at Hemsby, Norfolk on 22nd February, 1993.

Still, the waves are winning...

Sophisticated and expensive sea defences are in place along much of the east coast of England....but the waves are still winning. The surge of February, 1993 saw more of Norfolk and Suffolk slip into the sea; in fact several feet were lost between Covehithe and Lowestoft and the picture shows great cracks appearing at the end of a road which now goes nowhere. Soon, the large church of Covehithe will be in danger of joining its colleagues under the ocean as the edge of the cliff creeps nearer. Covehithe, once a thriving village of more than 300 people had a population of just 24 in 1993.

INDEX

Bob Ogley

BOB was a journalist for 30 years until leaving the editorship of the *Sevenoaks Chronicle* in 1989 to become a full-time publisher and author. The overnight success of his first book *In The Wake of The Hurricane*, which became a national bestseller in both editions, launched him into publishing in the nicest possible way and he has since written a further six books. In 1990 he wrote *Biggin on The Bump*, the history of the RAF fighter station at Biggin Hill, which received tremendous reviews from national, local and aviation press. The book raised £10,000 in author's royalties for the RAF Benevolent Fund. His latest effort is *Doodlebugs and Rockets - the Story of the Flying Bombs.*

Bob has raised a further £60,000 with the hurricane books for environmental charities and has discovered a supplementary career as a speaker to clubs and organisations. Recently he has teamed up with Ian Currie and Mark Davison to research, write and publish *The Kent Weather Book, The Sussex Weather Book, The Essex Weather Book* and now *The Norfolk and Suffolk Weather Book the* fifth of a new county weather series.

Ian Currie

THE ever-changing moods and patterns in our weather have always fascinated Ian Currie. He has vivid childhood memories of the 1958 thunderstorm and the deep winter snows of 1962-63, living then near Chislehurst in Kent. Sharing his interest with others has always been a feature of Ian's life. He writes a weekly weather column for several newspapers as well as being a weatherman for Radio Mercury and County Sound.

A graduate of Geography and Earth Science and teacher for 20 years, Ian is now a full-time writer and speaker to clubs and societies all over South-East England. He is a Fellow of the Royal Meteorological Society and a member of the Climatological Observers Link. Together with Mark Davison he has written *Surrey in The Hurricane, London's Hurricane* and *The Surrey Weather Book.* and *Red Sky at Night -Weather Sayings For All Seasons.*

Mark Davison

MARK has been in local journalism for 15 years and is currently deputy editor of the *Surrey Mirror Series.* He is co-author of three county books on weather events and has shown a keen interest in the climate since the big freeze of 1962-3 when, as a small child, he was spell-bound by the heavy falls of snow. In January 1987 his interest was totally renewed.

Risking whatever the elements might try and throw at him, he has ventured out on many wild nights to gather first-hand accounts of the South East's storms and freezes. Together with Ian Currie he has produced a set of postcards commemorating the severe cold spell in February, 1991.

Froglets' family

In The Wake of The Hurricane
(National Edition Hardback)
ISBN 0 9513019 4 2......................................£9.95

Surrey in The Hurricane
ISBN 0 9513019 2 6......................................£7.50

London's Hurricane
(Paperback) ISBN 0 9513019 3 4.................£4.95
(Hardback) ISBN 0 9513019 8 5.................£7.95

Eye on The Hurricane
(Eastern Counties)
(Paperback) ISBN 0 9513019 6 9.................£7.95
(Hardback) ISBN 0 9513019 7 7.................£11.95

King Oak of Sevenoaks
(A children's story)
ISBN 1 8723370 0 7 ....£6.95

Biggin On The Bump (The most
famous fighter station in the world).
(Hardback) ISBN 1 872337 10 4...............£10.95

The Surrey Weather Book
Published by Frosted Earth
ISBN 0 9516710 1 4...................................£7.50

The Sussex Weather Book
ISBN 1 872337 30 9...................................£9.95

The Kent Weather Book
ISBN   1 872337 35 X...............................£9.95

The Hampshire and Isle of Wight Weather Book
ISBN 1 872337 20 1...................................£9.95

The Essex Weather Book
ISBN 1 872337 66 X...............................£9.95

Doodlebugs and Rockets (The Battle
of the Flying Bombs)
(Hardback) ISBN 1 872337 22 8...............£16.95
(Paperback) ISBN 1 872337 21 X..............£9.95

Red Sky at Night
(Weather sayings for all seasons)
Published by Frosted Earth
ISBN 9516710 2 2......................................£4.95

To order any one of these books, please note that our address is **Froglets Publications, Brasted Chart, Westerham, Kent TN16 ILY.** TELEPHONE **0959 562972** FAX **0959 565365**